A VISUAL NOVEL OF THE WAR OF TOMORROW

ARCTIC STRIKE!

MICHAEL A. PALMER

AVON BOOKS NEW YORK

Acknowledgments: The author and editors wish to thank the Department of Defense and the Department of the Navy for providing photographs for this book. Most of the photographs of Soviet equipment have appeared in the DoD publication SOVIET MILITARY POWER. The editors wish to thank the Norwegian company NFT for its assistance.

A VISUAL NOVEL OF THE WAR OF TOMORROW: ARCTIC STRIKE! is an original publication of Avon Books. This work has never before appeared in book form. This is a work of fiction, and while it deals with actual weaponry and combat technology, the people and events are products of the author's imagination.

AVON BOOKS
A division of
The Hearst Corporation
105 Madison Avenue
New York, New York 10016

Published by arrangement with Bearsville Publishing Partnership
ISBN: 0-380-75844-X

Editor in Chief: Ian Ballantine
Series Editors: F. Clifton Berry, Jr., and Stephen P. Aubin
Art Director: Antonio Alcala
Design Assistant: Amy Korman
Produced by: FCB Associates, Washington, DC 20005

First Avon Books Trade Printing: February 1991

Printed in the U.S.A.

10 9 8 7 6 5 4 3 2 1

A VISUAL NOVEL OF THE WAR OF TOMORROW

ARCTIC STRIKE!

Target or hunter? KIROV class nuclear powered guided missile cruiser of the Soviet Northern Fleet sorties through the Barents Sea around Norway's North Cape from its base in the Kola Peninsula.

US Navy Seahawk SH-60B helicopter launches Penguin "fire and forget" antiship missile against Soviet frigate behind the island. The Penguin flies the course and finds its target on its own.

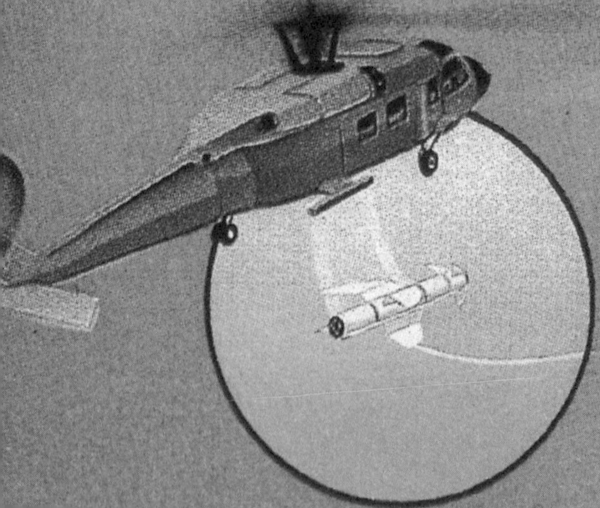

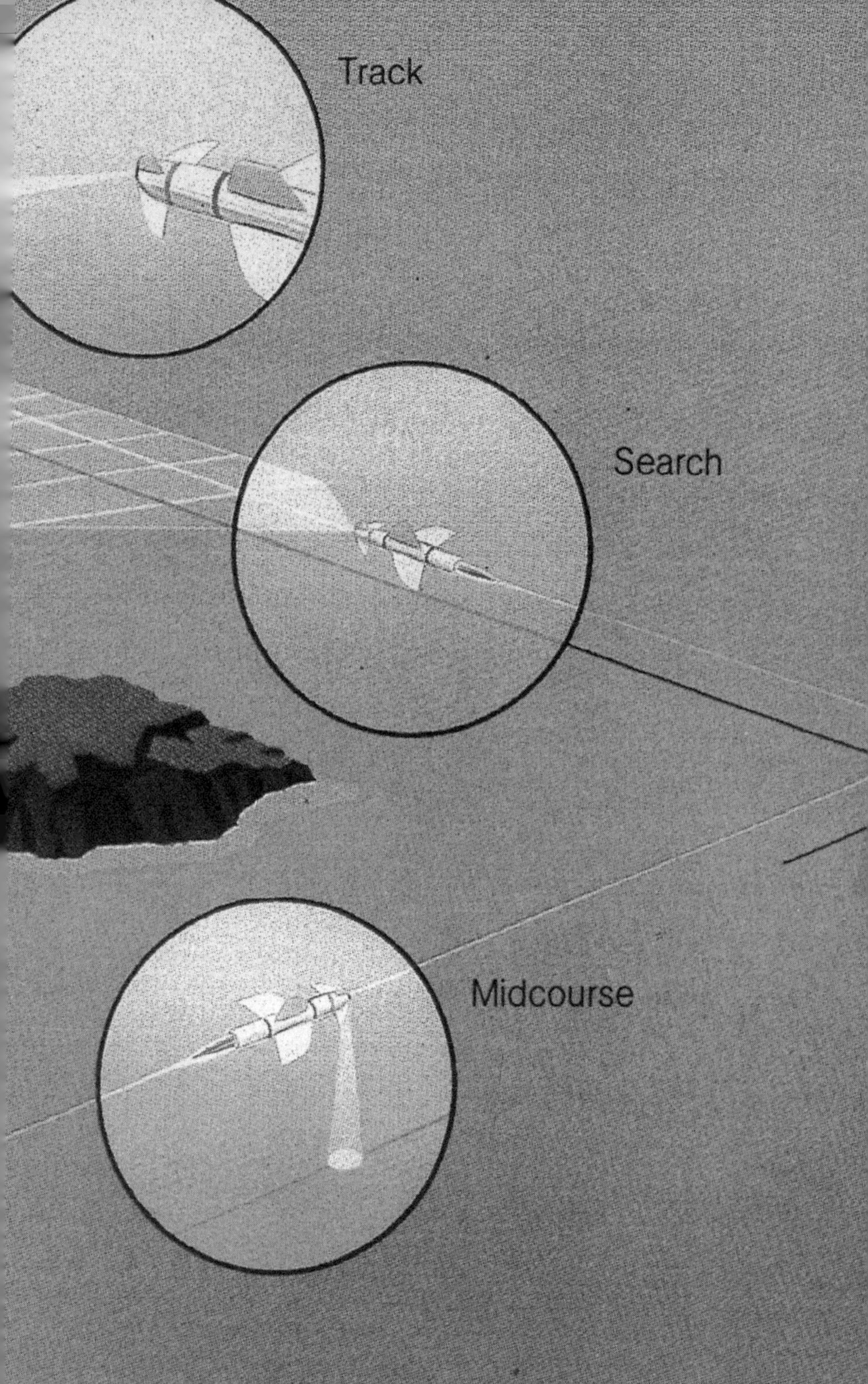
Track
Search
Midcourse

On the way!
US Navy STANDARD missile 2 blasts off its deck mount, heading for Soviet Northern Fleet ship over the horizon.

Contents

The Northern Flank: First Encounter

Royal Norwegian Air Force

Lieutenant Willi "Reds" Redmundson's F-16 Falcon was still climbing to 25,000 feet after lifting off from Bardufoss when four blips appeared on his radar, about forty miles ahead. "I've got four; do you have them, Andy?"

Andy was Redmundson's wingman, Second Lieutenant Rolf Andersen. "Roger, Reds."

Redmundson, the 339 KNL Squadron's self-professed "hottest" fighter jock, was reputed to have the reddest hair in all of Norway.

"Viking," Redmundson reported to his ground controller at Bardufoss, "we've got merge, four bogies, no IFF, flying 270, at 25,000. I've got 900 knots closure. We'll climb to Angels 15 and meet them."

Angels 15 indicated that Redmundson would take his section to 25,000 feet, by the code established for that day, 10,000 plus whatever the number reported.

"Roger, Reds. We repeat. Do not fire first. We do not, repeat, do not want to start anything."

Redmundson and Andersen had been briefed

Royal Norwegian Air Force F-16 Falcon on patrol. American and Norwegian Falcons played key roles in winning the war in the air over North Norway. The highly maneuverable F-16s are known as "Electric Jets" because of their computer operated "fly by wire," non-hydraulic controls.

before launch about the volatility of NATO-Soviet relations. The Ministry of Defense was determined that Norwegian forces not supply the Soviets with an excuse to start a war. But the planes Redmundson was about to intercept had overflown neutral Finland, and they were not Finnish.

Soviet reconnaissance planes had been overflying north Norway for days. Just the previous day, Redmundson and Andersen had intercepted a MiG-25. Overflights of a NATO country were provocative, but who wanted to precipitate the Third World War? Redmundson took a quick look back to make sure that Andersen, a green pilot if there ever was one, was still with him. He was. Redmundson leveled off at 25,000 feet. He had flown only for a few seconds when his radar warning light illuminated.

"Viking, Reds here. They've locked us up. Strong Doppler. Probably Foxhounds." Then to his wingman:

"Andy, safety off, lock'em up."

"Roger, Reds."

No sooner had Redmundson released his safety

than in quick succession the bogies began emitting IFF. Seconds later, Redmundson's missile warning rattle sounded. It was the warning for an "Amos," the Soviet AA-9 air-to-air missile. A medium range, all-aspect, radar homing, Mach 3 missile carried by MiG-31 Foxhounds.

"Amos lock-on," Redmundson yelled over his radio. "Stay with me."

Instinctively, Redmundson throttled up, lit his afterburner, and dove for the hard deck, hoping that radar return from the ground would confuse the missile. If it did not, a hard banking turn and chaff, with a Mach 4 closure, would give the Falcon its best chance for survival.

As Redmundson neared the ground, he could see missile contrails passing overhead. He pulled the stick back until the F-16 was nearly ballistic. Looking about, he noted that Andersen had failed to keep station.

"Andy, are you out there?"

Redmundson leveled off at 23,000 feet, killed the burner, and throttled back. A pair of fighters were dead ahead, nine miles, 1758 knots closure.

Soviet MiG-31 Foxhound. A redesign of the MiG-25 Foxbat, the Foxhound shares the high speed and poor maneuverability of its predecessor, but is capable of look-down attacks against low flying aircraft and cruise missiles.

He was too close for another Amos. Apparently, the Soviets had split up, a pair chasing each of the Norwegian Falcons. One against two constituted poor odds for a fighter pilot, but it was a situation for which Redmundson had trained. He flew right at the Soviets, waiting for them to make their move.

"No fighters in this bunch."

The Soviets were almost as green as Andersen. They neither tried to bracket Redmundson, nor to maneuver independently in a Loose Deuce. Red's Falcon tore by, right between the MiG-31s. "Foxhounds, Viking. I've got two."

He pulled back on the stick as he passed them and looped the Falcon. The Soviets were still turning to starboard. Redmundson dove and pulled in behind them. The leader pulled hard to turn inside the Norwegian fighter, but the Soviet wingman failed to keep up. Redmundson had a lock and fired an AIM-9L Sidewinder missile.

"Fox one."

Three seconds later the Sidewinder blasted into its target. The Soviet plane disintegrated.

Redmundson continued his 9.0-G turn until his vision blurred despite his best abdominal efforts to force blood up into his brain. He quickly realized he was blacking out and did a quarter roll to port, leveled off, pulled the stick back, and began a gentle roll to starboard. The high yo-yo brought him right into the rear-port quadrant of the MiG. He was still inverted when the lock indicator flashed. Redmundson righted the plane and fired his second Sidewinder. The Soviet pilot punched out flares, but the American-built missile was not to be deceived.

"Scratch two MiGs! Viking, this is Reds leader. Come in."

"Read you Reds. Good shooting. We lost Andy. We have large number contacts, bearing 090 from your position, 10,000 feet. Request fuel status."

"3600 pounds. Turning right to 090. Angels 15. Can I expect friendly company?"

"Roger, Reds."

Within a minute, Redmundson had the contacts on his screen. He had never seen so many at once. He thought he saw another Falcon, but he couldn't be sure. He climbed to 25,000 feet and then dove right into the Soviet armada, amazed at the sight of at least two score of IL-76 Candids and a few An-12 Cubs, all air transport aircraft, probably carrying paratroopers.

"Viking, this is Reds, have large, repeat multiple, many, bogies, Candids, Cubs, course 235. Engaging."

For Redmundson, it was the opportunity of a

AIM-9L Sidewinder missle. A heat-seeker, the sidewinder is reliable.

lifetime. Sitting ducks. And once in among the big, Soviet transports, he would be safe from enemy missiles. He swung right into the fleet of Candids, locked one up, and fired. Redmundson let loose his favorite Anglo-Saxon expletive as the Sidewinder dropped off the rail and failed to ignite. He pressed the switch a second time and the AIM-9 flew a perfect track to the Candid. Pieces of the aircraft, equipment, and Soviet soldiers hurtled by his plane. Missiles exhausted, Redmundson switched to guns, downing two more Candids.

"Shit Hot, I'm an Ace!" Redmundson remarked for the world to hear. But he had little time to savor his triumph. A pair of Soviet fighters were on his tail. Redmundson rolled and jinked as tracers slid by the canopy. The Soviets were no marksmen, but Redmundson's maneuvers took him out of the protective umbrella of the Soviet transports.

He was now low and slow, and dead meat for a missile. It was soon on him. He saw the warning light, heard the launch indicator, and pulled more Gs. Too late. His F-16 shuddered in a stall, then the missile slammed into it. A searing pain shot through Redmundson's right leg. He pulled the ejection handle as he passed out.

For Willi Redmundson in his parachute, the war was ending. He drifted to the ground and eventual internment in a Swedish hospital. But for his fellow Norwegians and their allies, the real war, the Third World War, was just beginning.

Willi Redmundson's F-16 was one of two Norwegian fighters able to penetrate the screen of Soviet interceptors that swept the skies of northern Norway in the early morning of 21 July. While the Fulcrums, Foxhounds, and Foxbats kept the Norwegian Air Force at bay, Soviet fighter-bombers and strike aircraft attacked airfields, ports, and command centers. Behind the waves of Soviet interceptors, the armada of IL-76s, carrying a brigade of the 76th Guards Airborne Division and a Spetsnaz commando detachment, made its way towards Bodo, a key NATO airfield, and nearby Reitan, headquarters of Commander Allied Forces North Norway (COMNON).

For the men of the Soviet 234 Guards "Black Sea" Airborne Brigade, the flight to Bodo was a nightmare. They had been trucked from their barracks to airfields around Pskov, about 300 miles south of Leningrad, in the late morning of 20 July and loaded into the transports. Throughout the summer afternoon, for no apparent reason, the planes sat in the sun, the paratroopers

Soviet Il-76 Candid loading Paratroopers of the 76th Guards Airborne Division.

sweltering. Eventually, the men were allowed to exit the planes and take shelter under the wings.

About 2230, after reembarking the men, the Candids took off, taking a wide berth of the Finnish border, hoping to escape detection, before turning west over the Kola. The transports overflew Finnish Lapland, skirting Sweden, and crossed the Norwegian border about 0345, turning west, fifteen minutes behind the Soviet interceptor screen. As the IL-76s crossed the Norwegian border and turned southwest for Bodo, the paratroopers had been cooped up in their transports for fifteen hours and had been airborne for five. Nerves were frayed, and the appearance of Norwegian fighters caused a near panic. Captain Sergei Kagan, who commanded a company of the 234 Guards, recalled:

We had made many jumps before, even combat jumps, some of us, in Afghanistan. But to be in the Ilyushin transport, and to know (as we did from the maneuvers the pilots were taking) that there were fighters about, was too much for some men. They wanted to jump right then and there. Right over the mountains from 10,000 feet. Anything to get out of the coffins we were in. But our major, he kept the men in line. I went up to the cockpit and saw the plane in front of us just blow apart as an F-16 went by. We were fortunate that so few of the enemy made it to us. Then our fighters arrived. After all of this, the assault landing held no fears for us.

The Candids continued on their way. Just north of Bodo, located on a small peninsula jutting out into the Salt Fiord, they turned west, passed the coast, and approached their objectives from northwest at an altitude of 450 feet.

Pillars of smoke indicated that the strike by Soviet Badgers had gone according to plan. The Soviet paratroopers began their low-level combat jumps. There was little surprise; nevertheless, the spirited, if uncoordinated, defense by the battalion-sized Norwegian unit defending the area proved to be no match for the Soviet paratroopers. By day's end, the airfield and the peninsula were secure.

The objective of the Spetsnaz detachment was COMNON headquarters at Reitan. The Soviet special forces unit, commanded by Major Ivan Istomin, landed about midway between the airfield and the headquarters. The security detachment at Reitan assumed, incorrectly, that the airfield was the Soviet objective and allowed themselves to be surprised by Istomin's unit.

"We stormed into the compound, everything according to plan," Istomin later told his interrogators. "I personally led the team to (General Lars) Hildegger's office. We burst in. He and an aide were burning documents in a waste basket. I yelled 'stop,' but he continued and one of my men gave them a burst from his assault rifle. It was a shame; a useless death. We had copies of all the important documents already."

The bold use of special forces hundreds of miles in NATO's rear was but one part of a daring plan for victory in the far north. With the elimination of the controlling headquarters for Norwegian and NATO forces in northern Norway, and the seizure of the airfield at Bodo, the Soviets had gained their most important objectives for their first day of the campaign in Norway. But other parts of the Soviet plan would be as difficult to execute. The failure of any one element could lead to the collapse of the entire operation.

The Soviet plan of operations on the Northern Flank was rooted in the grand strategy for the war as a whole, taking into account operational doctrine and the peculiar geography of the region.

The chain of events that ignited the Third World

War began in the West Bank city of Nablus on 28 June with the assassination of Israeli Minister of the Interior Mordechai Ravener by Syrian-trained PLO terrorists. The ensuing Israeli-Syrian war in southern Lebanon and the Golan, and the escalation of the crisis by the involvement of Libya and Iran, which provoked a confrontation with the United States, presented Soviet leaders with difficult choices.

Could the Kremlin sit back and watch two of its proxies be humiliated? Was Iran, already weakened by internal discord, to have its nose bloodied once again by the United States, possibly plunging it into a civil war from which a pro-American Pahlavi restoration might result? Such a course would only feed the growing perception of the Soviet Union as a declining power and further strengthen the image of the United States.

But what was to be done? A naval challenge to the United States and Israel in the Middle East would pit Russian weakness against American strength. Libya and Syria shared no border with the Soviet Union and could be supported only by sea. Unruly Iran seemed less an avenue of advance to the Persian Gulf than a potential Afghanistan on a grand scale.

Party Secretary and President Nikolai Golovnin favored broadening the war by invading Turkey—a NATO member—to open the Dardanelles, secure maritime communications to Libya and Syria, and to extend an overland route into the Levant. The Soviet military, including the Minister of Defense, Marshal Yuri Vladimirov, the Chief of the General Staff, and the Commander-in-Chief (CINC) of Warsaw Pact Forces, favored a global assault on the United States' allies around the entire Eurasian periphery.

Secretary Golovnin believed that the Soviet Union could invade Turkey without provoking a NATO response. According to one Soviet account, Golovnin is reputed to have remarked at an early July meeting of the GKO (State Committee of Defense): "What are they (NATO) going to do, invade Czechoslovakia and the GDR if we go into Turkey? Impossible."

But Minister of Defense Marshal Yuri Vladimirov considered the Party Secretary's views "naive." Vladimirov, a former CINC of Warsaw Pact Forces, judged the prospect of immediate NATO intervention remote but he expected the alliance at least to mobilize, a mobilization that would have to be met by the Soviet Union and its Warsaw Pact allies. In the event of a subsequent broadening of the war, which he considered inevitable, the Soviets would find that their chief asset, surprise, had been lost.

Vladimirov doubted that a superpower confrontation could be geographically contained to the Middle East. In a heated exchange with Secretary Golovnin, Vladimirov exclaimed:

Comrade Secretary, our submarines for the Mediterranean, and all of our ships if the Turks close the Strait, must come from the Kola. You know that! Do you really expect the Americans to watch us sail the Atlantic on our way to Gibraltar and not attack us until we pass the Straits? Do you think them fools? No! They will attack, and the war will widen. It cannot be otherwise. And then we will be forced to attack a prepared and fully mobilized NATO.

The alternatives as outlined by Vladimirov were stark: either strike the United States and its allies and accept the necessity of a global war, or retreat and watch the disintegration of Iran; the destruction, once again, of the Syrian army; and the removal of the Libyan madman, Colonel Mahmoud Gahlibi from power. Faced with such a difficult choice, Secretary Golovnin decided to continue his diplomatic efforts to defuse the situation. Events, however, had already begun to spin out of control.

The downing of the Pan American Boeing near Malta by a Libyan MiG so enraged the American public that the United States became determined to eliminate Gahlibi. With the active support of France, and the passive cooperation of Italy, American naval, amphibious, and air forces concentrated in the Central Mediterranean as a prelude to an invasion of the "shores of Tripoli."

The Israelis, stung by the killing of Ravener and Syrian use of surface-to-surface missiles (SSMs) against civilian targets, set their sights on the complete destruction of the Syrian army. And even within the Soviet camp, the Syrian president in Damascus, Colonel Gahlibi in Tripoli, and the radical Shi'a Mullahs in Teheran, fearing a Soviet "sell out," at the same time sensing that Soviet power was on the wane, were just as unwilling to respond to Golovnin's diplomatic overtures.

"The time for moderation is past, well past," Gahlibi proclaimed in his 14 July address before Libyan officer cadets. "The time to draw our swords, to seek redress for past wrongs, and to seek a final showdown in which Allah's will shall be made manifest, is upon us. We strike!"

If the "will" of the Almighty carried little weight in the Kremlin, the will of the military in the post-Glasnost Soviet Union was supreme. In fact, many Soviet military leaders recognized that their country, not the United States, was being buried. In private, Vladimirov was fond of quoting the American commentator George Will, who had termed the Soviet Union a second-class country, with third-rate leadership and a first-rate military.

From the earliest days of the reforms, it seemed the marshals understood that the economic and political decline of the Soviet Union, along with the turmoil in the Eastern European satellites, was bound to undermine Soviet military strength.

Mikhail Gorbachev's "perestroika" had opened a Pandora's Box within the Soviet Union and Eastern Europe that even the reassertion of state power from Moscow could only partially close. Vladimirov, along with many other Soviet military leaders, believed that the July crisis represented the last chance for the Soviets to use military strength to solve pressing economic and political problems—once and for all.

Vladimirov's solution was simple: initiate a global conventional war against the United States and its allies. Internally, such a struggle, if successful and kept short, would unify the peoples

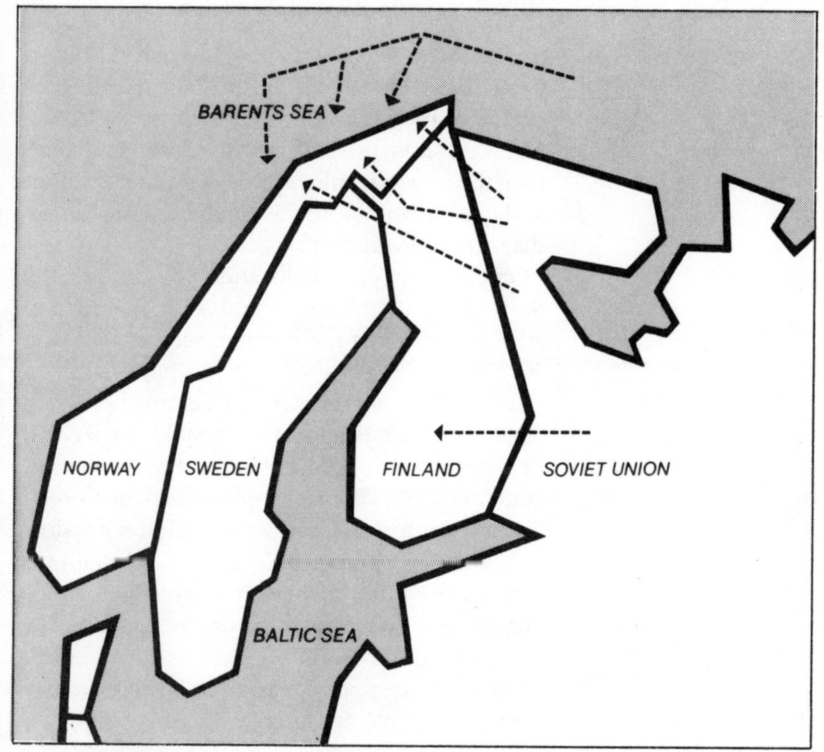

Northwestern TVD showing the directions of the Soviet offensive.

Norwegian F-16s were first to use Penguin missile in air-to-surface role. Other air forces followed suit, quickly gaining a new capability.

of the Soviet Union, and mute dissent in Eastern Europe. The Red Army would smash NATO on the Central Front, forcing the military collapse of the alliance and the withdrawal of the United States. A short, mobile campaign lasting no more than thirty days would destroy NATO's immediate ability to resist before the Americans could ship major reinforcements by sea.

On the European flanks and in the Pacific, the Soviets and their allies would seize positions of such strength that the prospects for a continued American struggle would appear hopeless.

The ultimate goal was not to destroy the United States, nor even to subjugate any additional Asian or European territories, but to drive the Americans back to the Western Hemisphere and the Central Pacific. Europe and East Asia, with the possible exception of China, would then be neutralized.

In the end, the defenseless capitalist nations around the Eurasian periphery would become tributary states, hostage to Russian military power and forced to support the stagnant Soviet economy through low-interest, long term "loans." Supreme on the battlefield, the Soviet Union would gain a new legitimacy, its military prowess overshadowing its economic and political failures.

At a GKO meeting held late in the evening of 13 July, Vladimirov's plan—code-named MONGOL—was accepted. The Third World War would begin on 21 July.

On the Defensive

South Varanger Garrison Draws Blood

Lieutenant Colonel Thoms Thomson could not believe his eyes. Standing on the hood of his Bv-202 command vehicle, perched on the high ground east of Kirkenes, he could see far eastward across the Soviet border clear to Pechenga. The evening was unusually clear, twilight still a good half-hour distant in the land of the midnight sun. Below him, the road from Pechenga to the Norwegian border was filled with the tanks and other vehicles of the Soviet 45th Corps.

Thomson turned to his aide, Captain Lars Knutsun, and handed him the binoculars.

"Take a look, Lars. A fantastic sight. What we couldn't do with a few TOWs, no? But we must not provoke them."

"That would stir them up, sir."

"And slow them down tomorrow, but we wouldn't want to do that. They line up an entire corps at our border and those fools in Oslo worry about provocation. What, I might ask, is this? Well, we'll get them in the morning."

"Yes, but the morning fog will hide them, Colonel. Now would be the time."

"But the fog will hide us, too. We'll have a few wrinkles for them."

Thomson commanded the South Varanger Garrison (SVG), the Norwegian Army unit responsible for the defense of the border with the Soviet Union. His job was not to halt an attack, an impossible task for a battalion, but to delay and to extract as high a cost as possible from the assaulting force. If he could hold the Soviets long enough, perhaps only forty-eight hours, the Finnmark Brigade's three Home Guard battalions would have time to mobilize.

Despite the reluctance of the Norwegian government to order mobilization, the men of the northern counties had taken matters into their own hands. In fact, the 2nd Battalion of the Finnmark Brigade had all but mobilized by the evening of 20 July.

In Kirkenes, reservists began guarding the airfield, bridges, and command centers. Throughout the day, as news of the Soviet concentration across the border spread through the county, the reservists packed their families into their cars, the buses of the Nord-Norge-Bussen line, coastal steamers, or airplanes for a trip to the south and, they hoped, safety.

Unordered, many men then began to report to their units. Thomson allowed them to ready their vehicles and equipment and move out of the depots, although he kept the men in civilian clothes. This early mobilization allowed Thomson to move the SVG into the area east of the town. His regulars knew the country intimately and had prepared a few surprises for the Soviets.

Farther south, motorized columns of the Soviet 54th Corps had lined up for thirty miles along the roads leading to the Finnish border west of Kandalaska. If the dispositions of the corps did not provide the Finns with notice of Soviet intentions, the arrival in Helsinki of two Special Emissaries from the Soviet government certainly did. They were there "to consult with representatives of the Finnish people at this time of severe crisis," under the terms of the Soviet-Finnish friendship treaty of 1948.

In a meeting with Finnish President Urho Maaken, the Soviet officials "requested" that their forces be given entry into Finland to forestall belligerent movements through the small neutral country directed toward the Soviet Union.

President Maaken faced a difficult dilemma. He was loathe to allow Soviet forces into his country or to permit the Soviets' use of Finland as an avenue for an assault on his Scandinavian neighbors. But to refuse the request seemed likely to force a Soviet invasion and probable bloody occupation.

Secretly, he saw that warnings of the Soviet request were passed to the Norwegians and Swedes, while units of the Finnish armed forces were alerted and ordered to defend themselves and Finnish territory if attacked. Maaken hoped to force the Soviets to show their hand before committing himself and his country one way or the other.

At 0330, as the main offensive began along the Inter-German Border, the Soviet 54th Corps began a two-pronged advance into Finland. The right-hand column of two brigades drove along the Knolayarvi-Sodankyla-Muonio road. At Muonio, the road turned north along the Swedish border, through the Finnish Wedge, and into Norway. The 54th Corps' two left-hand brigades drove along the Knolayarvi-Rovaniemi-Tornio axis toward the Gulf of Bothnia, a movement that would cover the flank of the advance into Norway, effectively blocking against Finnish reinforcements that might try to move north.

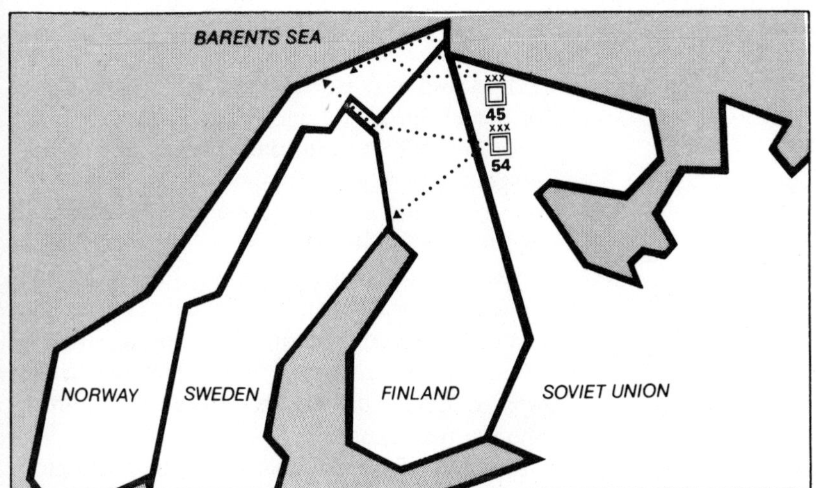

The advance of the 45th and 54th Corps, aimed at isolating North Norway.

Simultaneously in the north, the Soviet 45th Corps struck west in two columns. The southernmost column of two brigades moved from the Nautsi area along the road to Ivalo, south of Lake Inari, before turning north for the Tana River bridge along the Finnish-Norwegian border and Karasjok. From there, the brigades would move north to Lakselv at the head of the Porsangen Fiord, overrunning the airfield at Banak and cutting the E-6.

The other two brigades of the 45th Corps took the direct route into Norway. Mixed assault teams advanced along the Pechenga-Kirkenes axis and the Nautsi-Svanvik road that approached Kirkenes from the south, while two battalions of the 63rd "Kirkenes" Naval Infantry Brigade staged a heliborne and amphibious assault in the Norwegian rear area. The 63rd Brigade had taken Kirkenes in a hastily staged amphibious attack in 1944, thus earning its official title.

The landing of the 234th Guards Airborne Brigade at Bodo has already been described. Unfortunately for the Soviets, the planned landings at Narvik and Tromso were canceled because of last minute changes in Norwegian dispositions.

The Soviet plan had called for the lead battalions of the 234th, 237th, and 239th brigades of the 76th Guards to land at Bodo, Tromso, and Narvik respectively. These battalions were loaded in transports and were prepared to take off when photos from MiG-25 intelligence overflights revealed Norwegian troop movements that caused concern at Northwest Front headquarters. The main Norwegian field force in the north, Brigade North, had been spread in an arc covering the approaches to the Fortress Norway area from the north and east.

But late on the 19th, COMNON, who considered a Soviet special forces assault more of an immediate threat than an overland attack along the E-6 or E-78, which could not materialize for days, moved the 1st Battalion back towards Brigade headquarters at Bardufoss, near Andselv, the 2nd to the Tromso area, and the 3rd to Narvik, reinforcing the small garrisons guarding these critical air and sea bases.

Northwest Front, apprised of these moves in the early afternoon of the 20th, cancelled the drops at Tromso and Narvik. Lacking sufficient lift to move the entire 76th Division on the first day, because of heavy demands for transports for operations in Denmark, Germany, against the Turkish Straits, and in the Middle East, Northwest Front considered it too risky to drop individual battalions amidst equal numbers of Norwegian regulars. The plan was changed, with the lead battalions of the 237th and 239th brigades disembarking, and the second and third battalions of the 234th embarking for a brigade-sized assault on Bodo.

After securing Bodo on the 21st, the 2nd and 3rd battalions of the 234 Guards moved east along the road to Finneid, which they reached late in the evening of 22 July. The E-6 highway was cut and ground communications between north and south Norway were severed.

Additional Soviet airmobile battalions moved by helicopter into Finnmark. Mi-8 transport helicopters lifted one battalion to Karasjok, taking the town from a surprised handful of defenders, while a detached company seized the Tana River bridge. Other helicopters lifted three Soviet battalions to Tana, Seida, and Nyborg.

The direct Soviet drive down the E-6, heavily supported by tanks, fell afoul of the defenders of Lieutenant Colonel Thomson's battalion, the South Varanger Garrison. During the 20th, Thomson made a very visible show of force along the high

Soviet Mi-8 Hip helicopter serves in both attack and transport versions in tactical regiments.

Soviet T-80 Main Battle Tank with reactive armor. Soviet tanks fared poorly in the restrictive terrain of North Norway.

ground overlooking the Soviet border. But as the fog rolled in, he pulled his men back. As he had expected, the Soviets pounded the abandoned Norwegian positions with artillery just as they opened their attack at 0330.

At that point, Thomson's men were dispersed, waiting in ambush along suspected avenues of advance.

"We had some help from General Fog," Thomson later wrote. "His vapors hid us from the Russians, he slowed their advance to a crawl, and he kept their helicopter gunships off our back."

The men of Thomson's battalion were in positions well back from the border but within 200 to 600 meters of the road to Kirkenes. The Soviet advance

along either side of the road proceeded slowly, slowed by terrain, mines, and fog. A mixed column of T-80 tanks and APCs advanced along the road itself and made better time until it encountered a broken down American-built M-113 APC. The lead BTR-60 attempted to bypass the M-113 but struck a mine and was soon a wreck itself. The Soviet column then halted and began to shift a T-55 tank outfitted with a bulldozer blade to the front.

As the old tank began to shove the wreck off the road, the booby-trapped APC exploded, releasing a huge fireball that enveloped the would-be dozer. At that signal, the Norwegians began firing rockets at the column, knocking out tanks, BMPs, and other vehicles.

"The visibility was so poor," one Norwegian soldier wrote, "that we had to move close to the road to see the Russians, too near to use our ATGMs which you couldn't control at such ranges. But our rockets did good work."

A Russian tank officer later recalled:

The fog was so bad, you couldn't see men more than maybe 100 meters off, even if they were standing in the road. Our lasers (range finders on the main tank guns) didn't work. All we saw were the flashes from the enemy rockets as they were fired. We called for suppressive fire, but the enemy changed positions before that arrived. We couldn't get air support. So we had to get the men out of the BMPs and have them clear the ground on either side of the road. That worked, but it slowed us down considerably.

Opposite: Typhoon class nuclear missile subs entered service in 1983. They are huge, displacing 25,000 tons.

Gradually, as the pressure from Soviet infantry mounted, and supplies of anti-tank rockets dwindled, the Norwegians withdrew. Once the fog lifted, however, they resumed their attacks with the longer-range ATGMs. Only the arrival of Soviet forces moving astride the road, combined with support from helicopter gunships whose pilots braved the thinning fog, finally drove off the Norwegians. They retired in fair order to wooded areas where they could not easily be pursued, there to draw upon stocks of buried ammunition and food that allowed them to continue to harass the Soviets for weeks.

By the evening of 21 July, the advance elements of the 45th Corps reached Kirkenes. A smart attack, coordinated with an air and sea assault by two battalions of the 63rd Naval Infantry, drove the 2nd battalion of the Finnmark Brigade from the town and opened the E-6 road. By late on 22 July, lead elements of the Corps were twenty miles west of Kirkenes. But the Soviets

had suffered more than 800 killed and wounded and the loss of forty tanks and APCs at the hands of the Norwegian defenders.

By the evening of the 24th, Soviet mechanized columns had driven deep into Finnish Lapland and the Norwegian Fydde. Farther south, the 54th Corps reached the Gulf of Bothnia and Muonio along the Swedish border. While the Finns made no effort to attack the left wing of the Corps at Tornio, the Pohjan Brigade took up positions behind the Simo River, forcing the Soviets to maintain their flank guard. In northern Norway, the 45th Corps had overrun Finnmark. The 234th Guards had taken Bodo and cut the E-6. But already there were indications that the Soviet plan was beginning to unravel.

Colonel Nikolai Vorontsev, a Stavka staff officer, who helped develop the plans for the Northwestern Front, commented:

We had always considered the first forty-eight hours of the advance the most critical. Now, we had had successes--Bodo, Tornio, Karasjok, Tana. But we had been forced to alter our plans for the 76th Guards Airborne, cancelling the planned drops at Narvik and Tromso. The Finns had resisted our advance, costing us losses and time and forcing the 54th Corps to keep two brigades along the Kemi River line. And while we had stormed Kirkenes, it had taken an entire day longer than we had planned. We had hoped to have the 45th Corps reach Tana and join up with the airmobile battalions. But they were a good 160 kilometers short of their objectives on the night of the 22nd. And the whole time, the Norwegians were mobilizing. More and more we realized that the battle was going to be decided at sea, by the navies and the air forces.

The Soviet advance had disrupted the mobilization of the Finnmark Brigade. The depots of the 1st

Battalion in the Tana area were overrun by the surprise Soviet airmobile landings. The 2nd Battalion was destroyed in the fighting for Kirkenes. Only the 3rd Battalion at Lakselv managed to take the field fully armed and prepared for battle, only to begin an immediate retreat.

Farther south, a battalion-group at Alta and the 15th Brigade at Narvik, mobilized. Within forty-eight hours the battalions of the latter formation were stretched along the E-6 from Narvik to Bardufoss. Perhaps most significantly, KNL C-130 transports managed to fly a reserve battalion from Oslo to Bardufoss during the afternoon of 21 July, despite intense Soviet air activity and efforts to shut down the northern airfields.

By the evening of 22 July, Fortress Norway was beginning to fill with friendly troops. Nine battalions, a division equivalent, were already taking up positions. Another three were deployed farther north where they would inflict additional delays on the 45th Corps. The slowed advances of the 54th and 45th Corps placed an even greater premium on the ability of the Northern Fleet to prevent the further reinforcement of northern Norway by sea.

Other than the air landings and the Spetsnaz assault on COMNON headquarters, the Soviet movements surprised no one. Clearly, Soviet commanders in the far north made a conscious decision that speed, not surprise, was more important on their front. Lieutenant General Georgi Bagdasarian, commander of the 45th Corps, later commented:

Oh, yes, of course, Maskirovka. Surprise and deception were all well and good in Germany. They had multiple axes of advance and they had night to cover their movements. They thought that attacking on an eight-kilometer front was a narrow advance for a corps. In the north, we had, at best,

Sailor enters hatch of US Navy attack sub; the US and Royal Navy submarines haunted the Northern Fleet.

two roads for a corps, usually one. My axis of advance was often the width of the E-6, one tank wide. And you frequently couldn't deploy your vehicles off the road. If the ground wasn't swampy, it was mountainous. So we packed our troops along the road right up to the border on 20 July. The alternative was to move them forward a few hours before the attack, but that meant assembling the troops in the fog, and probable confusion. Instead, by putting them right at the border in their attack positions, we could assault at once, and use the fog to cover our advance.

And, let me remind you, we were in a hurry. Stavka said: "Cover your preparations; surprise is the key." But Stavka also said: "You've got to get to the paratroopers, we want you at Bodo in a fortnight." I concluded that for every six hours delay, I would face another battalion at Skibotn. So I put everything up front. In my view it was a race. The 54th did the same, I believe.

The initial Soviet attacks were well-planned and executed. Nevertheless, small detachments of Finnish border guards felled trees, blew bridges, and laid mines in an attempt to slow Soviet progress. In spite of such delaying tactics, the 54th Corps' advance on Rovaniemi, the Soviets' southernmost drive, reached the outskirts of the town within the first forty-eight hours, an advance of over 100 miles as the crow flies, but almost 150 road miles. Early on the 23rd, elements of a Finnish air defense battalion and some light troops were driven from the town as the Soviet column pushed on to the Gulf of Bothnia, which it reached on the afternoon of the 24th.

The northern column of the 54th Corps advanced well over fifty miles the first day, struggling more with the breakdown of its own vehicles than with Finnish resistance. By the afternoon of the 22nd, elements of the lead brigade reached Sodankyla, meeting the first, and only, significant Finnish resistance of the campaign.

Soviet intelligence had been unable to pinpoint the exact location of the Lappi Jager Battalion but expected to find it covering Rovaniemi. Aerial reconnaissance photos showed clearly a concentration of military vehicles in the town.

But the Finnish commander, Major Hansi Halsua, had moved his unit north to Sodankyla, leaving most of his Soviet-built APCs conspicuously in Rovaniemi. Halsua, whose grandfather and uncle had been captured in the Soviet Winter War of 1939-1940 and had disappeared in the Gulag, and whose father had fought under Marshal Mannerheim, was determined to extract as high a price as possible from the invading Soviets. Delaying their advance into Norway would do just that.

The lead battalion of the Soviet 81st Motor Rifle Brigade (MRB) passed through Sodankyla, speeding along the road, until it ran into an obstruction about ten kilometers outside of town defended by a Finnish platoon. Traffic along the road soon came to a halt. At that signal, with the sounds of firing reaching the town, Halsua's Jagers surprised the 81st MRB's 2nd battalion in the streets of Sodankyla, while a detached company attacked the lead elements of the 3rd battalion. The Finns used French SS-11 ATGMs (anti-tank guided missiles) and Soviet-built 55mm recoilless rifles against the Soviet BMP's. Within minutes a score of Soviet vehicles were burning.

Throughout the afternoon and into the evening, the Soviets counterattacked. The 1st Battalion reversed direction and came to the aid of its sister battalion, while the 118th MRB stood stalled along the road, prevented from joining the battle by the swampy terrain.

The arrival late in the afternoon of Su-17 Fitter ground attack aircraft finally broke Finnish resistance. By the twilight that passed for nightfall in the far north, the town was securely in Soviet hands. But the 2nd and 3rd battalions of the 81st MRB had been mauled and henceforth were used to guard the rear of the division's advance.

Major Halsua, who later rose to the rank of general, commented:

I have often been asked about my "Halsua" tactics. They were not original. In fact, I learned them from my father, who had learned them during the 1939-40 war. They had called them "Motti" or "pocket" tactics, although they used them on a larger scale. The basic concept was to maximize the use of restrictive terrain and off-road mobility against a highly mechanized but road-bound enemy. In my father's day, snow kept the Russians on the road. In my day, since we fought in the summer, I used the swamps. But the concept was the same. And perhaps the Russians were the same, too.

The Soviets spent the 23rd of July clearing the road of wrecks and resting exhausted men. Not until the afternoon of 26 July did the 118th MRB reach the Norwegian border. While half of Halsua's 500 men were killed or captured, the major and his remaining Jagers escaped to the north. For the rest of the campaign, they continued to harass Soviet supply columns.

Northern Fleet Attacks

NATO Navies Strike Back

Soviet surface forces and submarines bore the initial brunt of the confrontation with NATO in the North Atlantic. The morning of 21 July found Soviet Naval Aviation Badgers and Backfires attacking Norwegian airfields between Banak and Bodo, not conducting deep strikes against NATO naval assets in the North Atlantic. Because many of the ten airfields struck that morning were beyond the effective range of Northwest Front and Archangel Air Defense Sector ground attack aircraft, the long-range SNA bombers were pressed to the fill that role.

Meanwhile, two Soviet surface strike groups (KUGs), an anti-submarine warfare group (KPUG), and a half-dozen submarines began the war in the Norwegian Sea. The KUGs comprised the heart of the Northern Fleet. KUG 1 consisted of the new nuclear carrier *Tblisi*, operating with the powerful Kirov-class battle cruiser *Frunze*, two other cruisers, and two destroyers. KUG 2 consisted of the Kresta II-class guided-missile cruiser *Kronstadt*, four other cruisers, two destroyers, two frigates, the Missile Support Ship *General Ryabakov,* and submarine tender *Fyodor Vidyaev.* KPUG 1 consisted of the Kara-class cruiser *Nikolayev* and three destroyers. The three groups were operating north of Tromso about 150 miles from the Norwegian coast.

Throughout the day on 20 July, Norwegian P-3Bs of the 333rd Squadron, based at Andoya, tracked the Soviet groups while four Norwegian diesel submarines sparred with KPUG 1's destroyers and frigates.

Meanwhile, Rear Admiral Johan Larsen, commanding the Norwegian squadron at Olavsvern (Tromso), readied the frigates *Oslo* and *Stavanger,* and a dozen Hauk and Snogg-class, Penguin-armed fast attack craft to sail with the fog. Larsen intended to open hostilities at sea. The rear admiral's chief of staff later wrote:

The Tblisi was like a magnet to Larsen. He was determined to sink her, to have the Norwegian Navy destroy the Soviets' newest major ship of war. We sailed from Olavsvern with the fog. It was something we had practiced often. Even the

The Soviet battle cruiser Kirov in the Norwegian Sea. The largest surface combatants built since the end of the Second World War, Kirov-class battle cruisers suffered the fate of their smaller cousins when caught without air cover at sea.

Soviet Sovremennyy-class destroyer. This class of large destroyers were built primarily for anti-surface warfare and were poor platforms for ASW.

Soviet "trawler" had moved off, afraid of running aground. Had she not, I think that Larsen might well have sunk her. He was certain that the war was about to begin. We turned south, maintaining strict emissions control, and then came back north.

AWACS monitored the Soviets' movements and we received the data we needed to track them. We monitored our radios, waiting for word of the Soviet attack. Larsen was determined not to get caught in port, or be surprised. We stayed just within missile range.

The Soviets were also observing strict silence, but they thought we were still in port. Then, at 0330, we received word that there were air battles raging in the north. The admiral gave the signal and the ships all turned everything on and began firing at will. Either we had surprised the Soviets or they just failed to react as fast as we had.

In spite of Larsen's determination, the uncoordinated Norwegian attack did little damage. One Penguin SSM hit and severely damaged the Sovremennyy-class destroyer *Osmotritelnyy.* But

poor execution by nervous, inexperienced operators, complicated further by effective Soviet countermeasures and defensive efforts, caused the SSMs to miss.

NATO submarines achieved somewhat better results. The cruiser *Marshal Timoshenko* was damaged and the crippled *Osmotritelnyy* sunk.

The NATO Penguin anti-ship missile. Penguin-armed helicopters, aircraft, and surface ships helped defeat Soviet surface forces off the Norwegian coast.

The US Navy's SSN *Skipjack* joined the attack later in the morning, launching a pair of wire-guided Mark 48 torpedoes meant for the *Tblisi*, but which struck and sank the destroyer *Udaloy*.

During these initial engagements in the Norwegian Sea, the Soviet centralized command system responded poorly to the demands placed upon it by the chaotic surface and subsurface actions being carried out hundreds of miles from the Fleet Command Post. Nevertheless, the Soviet quantitative edge began to tell. Too many ships. By noon, Soviet SSMs had sunk eight of the twelve Norwegian attack craft and the frigate *Stavanger*, while KPUG 1 attacks damaged the Norwegian submarine *Kya*, and the American *Skipjack*.

Farther south, a Soviet Victor III-class SSN tracked Standing Naval Force Atlantic (STANAVFORLANT), a multi-national NATO force consisting of the Dutch frigate *Kortenaer* (flying the flag of Rear Admiral Pieter Van Wynt), the German destroyer *Molders*, the American frigate *Moinester*, the Canadian destroyer *Iroquois*, and the British frigate *Active*, steaming along the Norwegian coast near Trondheim. One Type-65 torpedo sank the *Moinester*. Van Wynt promptly withdrew into Trondheim. Through the afternoon and evening, NATO continued to counterattack. The Royal Navy SSN *Spartan* exacted revenge by sinking the Victor that had torpedoed the *Moinester*. Meanwhile, RAF Phantoms and Buccaneers that had staged to Orland in the morning, were thrown into hasty strikes against KUG 1, only to be driven off by the *Tblisi*'s Flankers. A dozen RAF aircraft failed to return from these raids. The Soviets lost one Flanker and three Forgers.

Undaunted, Larsen's *Oslo* and four remaining patrol craft struck the Soviets again, damaging the replenishment vessel *Riyabakov*. Two hours later, the British SSN *Conqueror* finished it off,

Soviet Udaloy-class destroyer. This class of destroyers were designed primarily for ASW.

before falling prey itself and suffering severe, though not fatal, damage at the hands of a Soviet Alfa-class submarine. SSM attacks by KUGs 1 and 2 destroyed the *Oslo*, killing Rear Admiral Larsen. Shortly thereafter, Soviet Naval Aviation made its appearance when a squadron of Badgers caught the remaining Norwegian attack boats retiring to Tromso and sank all four. Il-38 May aircraft detected and sank the Norwegian submarines *Stadt* and *Kya*, while helicopters from the *Tblisi* contacted and damaged the Norwegian submarine *Sklinna*.

At the end of the first day, NATO surface forces had been decisively driven from the Norwegian Sea. STANAVFORLANT refueled and left Trondheim in company with the Norwegian frigates *Bergen* and *Narvik*. After this confrontation, Van Wynt wisely was less than eager to venture too far north. While submarines of both sides were still at large in the Norwegian Sea, NATO had suffered the heaviest losses: three submarines sunk and three damaged, all for the destruction of a single Soviet submarine.

By the evening of 21 July, Kontra-Admiral Valentin Rybokov, flying his flag in the *Tblisi*, felt confident enough to attempt limited at-sea replenishment for his vessels in preparation for covering the movement south of a Soviet Landing Force (OV), which by midnight had sailed from Pechenga and neared the North Cape.

The force and effectiveness of the Soviet naval

Patrol areas of the submarines USS Jack and HMS Warspite.

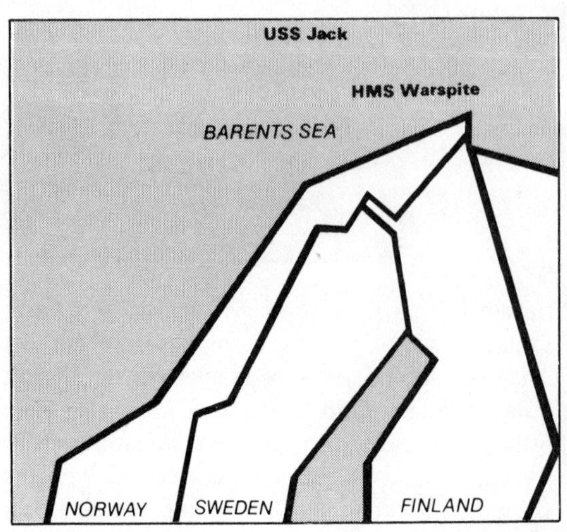

assault in the Norwegian Sea during the 21st raised concerns at Submarine Force Eastern Atlantic Area (SUBEASTLANT) over the fate of two NATO boats dispatched several days earlier into the Barents Sea. For Captain John Jordan, commander of the American Permit-class submarine *Jack*, and Captain Lucas Yeo, commander of the British Valiant-class submarine *Warspite*, the war began about 250 miles north of Murmansk. Their mission was to attack Soviet vessels leaving Kola bases for operations farther south. Though not part of any determined effort to penetrate the Soviet bastion area and attack Soviet SSBNs, the two submarines were given general directions of movement that would keep the *Jack* to the north and the *Warspite* to the south, hopefully out of each other's path. Any targets contacted would be assumed to be Soviet.

The ultimate loss of both submarines makes it difficult to piece together a picture of their operations. During the afternoon of the 21st, according to Soviet sources, the SSN *Desna* was apparently torpedoed by a NATO submarine, probably the *Warspite*, about 200 miles north of Murmansk. The loss of the old Echo II-class boat caused a sharp Soviet response.

The Northern Fleet KPF vectored a half-dozen SSN attack subs to hunt for what the Soviets mistakenly assumed were six NATO submarines active in the area. Later on the 21st, one of the hunters became the hunted, when the *Vera Figner* was damaged by a torpedo probably fired by the southernmost NATO boat, the *Warspite*.

By evening, three squadrons of Be-12 ASW aircraft had joined the hunt, a six-frigate KPUG was detached from the escort of the OV transporting the Soviet Naval Infantry battalions round the North Cape to hunt the NATO subs, and a second seven-frigate KPUG sailed from Archangelsk.

It appears that these Soviet attacks drove the *Warspite* north and east, while the *Jack* continued to operate north of Murmansk. By morning, three squadrons, one of Bears and two of Il-38 Mays, were also committed to the hunt. The KPUG that had sailed from Archangelsk claimed an attack and kill early on the 22nd not far from the entrance to the White Sea.

If a NATO submarine was operating in this area, it must have been the *Warspite*. But the reports of her demise were apparently exaggerated, for on the afternoon of the 22nd, the Soviet SSBN *Kolskiy* was torpedoed, severely damaged, and forced to return to Severodinsk for emergency repairs. Again, the *Warspite* was the probable culprit.

About the same time, 350 miles to the west, the Soviet SSN *Mikhail Kalinin* claimed a kill. This second Soviet kill, of six later claimed, was probably an attack on the *Jack*. Perhaps damaged, but definitely not sunk, the *Jack* turned the tables and torpedoed the *Mikhail Kalinin* three hours later. Damaged, the Soviet boat returned to port.

The *Warspite*, unfortunately, was not so lucky. She was torpedoed and sunk by the two Soviet subs in a coordinated attack. The Soviets then turned all their efforts on the *Jack*. At 1700 on the 23rd, the *Vasily Chuykov* apparently finished off the American submarine about 350 miles north of the North Cape.

While the loss of two NATO submarines was a tactical defeat, the dispatch of the boats into the Barents Sea nevertheless represented an operational victory for NATO. Vice Admiral Sir Gary Weir, who as COMSUBEASTLANT planned and directed the operation, later explained his thinking before the Royal United Service Institute:

There have been those who have suggested that the submarines were "wasted." I think not. Yes, we did lose two submarines for one of the enemy's. But three others were damaged, mission kills, if you will. Six attack submarines that might profitably have been employed farther south in the Norwegian Sea were kept busy for three critical days. They spent the fourth returning to port to replenish their torpedoes. Not until the 29th were they available for operations farther south. Over a dozen Soviet frigates, half of them stripped from their amphibious force headed for Andoya, were kept off the Kola. By Soviet accounts about three score of ASW aircraft were busy during the war's first seventy-two hours hunting our "six" submarines. None of those brave submariners died in vain. Their efforts helped make victory in the Norwegian Sea possible.

As Soviet air, surface, and subsurface forces battled for control of the Norwegian and Barents seas, farther south and west Soviet submarines struck at the North Atlantic sea lanes. Several of these running battles involved convoys bringing critically important equipment and supplies to Norwegian ports.

The frigate *Trippe* spent most of the 20th of

July tracking a Soviet Oscar-class SSN that had been shadowing a large American-Canadian convoy. It included one destroyer, five frigates, and seven Military Sealift Command (MSC) vessels steaming about 400 miles south of Cape Farewell, carrying important Marine Corps equipment and supplies to Norway.

The *Trippe*, unfortunately, lost contact with the Oscar shortly after 0200 on the 21st when the frigate's old Seasprite helicopter suffered a loss of oil pressure and had to return to the ship. So Commander Edward Fox decided to head toward the last known position of the Oscar while the maintenance detachment attempted to repair the chopper.

"We had continued along the last bearing for an hour and a half," Fox told a Navy Board of Inquiry, "when we received news that the war had begun."

What Fox did not know was that in the interim the Soviet submarine, which held an 8-knot speed advantage over the American Knox-class frigate, had slipped behind the *Trippe* where the baffles,

The American frigate Trippe before the war. A Knox-class ship, her top speed was only 27 knots.

a blind zone caused by the noise of a ship's engines and screws, hid it from Fox's sonar.

At 0337 a single torpedo, "probably a Type 65," struck the *Trippe*'s stern. "We were dead in the water almost instantly, flooding, listing, and obviously sinking," Fox recalled. Having little choice, he ordered an appropriate message sent and then gave the order to Abandon Ship.

Based on reports from the Oscar, the Northern Fleet KPF was able to vector two additional SSNs into attack positions. Soon thereafter, the American frigates *McInerney* and *Jack Williams,* the Canadian destroyer *Huron*, and frigate *Ottawa* were sunk. Two of the attacking Soviet submarines were also destroyed, an Oscar by the frigate *Stephen W. Groves,* and a Victor by P-3 Orions from Keflavik.

About 400 miles to the east, a second American-Canadian convoy fell victim to even heavier attacks by five Soviet submarines. In that attack, the Canadian frigate *Nipigon* and the chartered cargo ship (AK) *TransColumbia* were sunk, while the American Perry-class frigate *John L. Hall* was damaged by a Type ET-80 wire-guided torpedo. Only one Soviet submarine suffered damage.

The heavy losses inflicted on these two convoys—seven ships out of twenty-six and one damaged—concerned SACLANT, Admiral Sean Maloney, in Norfolk. While American and Canadian escorts had managed to keep the Soviets away from the supply vessels, except for the *TransColumbia*, the heavy escort losses could not be sustained. Would the Soviets be able to finish off the convoys on the 22nd? They were still 400 to 500 miles from Iceland and safety.

At 0126 on the 22nd, two torpedoes struck the *Hawes* and broke the frigate in two. When SACLANT learned of the latest loss, he remarked, "It looks like we're in for another bad day."

An American F/A-18 Hornet launches from the aircraft carrier Coral Sea.

But, almost miraculously, the tempo of the Soviet attacks slowed. No further ships were lost, and by evening both convoys were within fifty miles of Reykjavik.

The sudden respite was not the result of Soviet largess. Iceland-based P-3s sank and damaged several Soviet submarines, forcing many others away from the convoys. Additionally, as early as the 22nd, many Soviet submarines had exhausted their supply of torpedoes. Captain Third Class Vasily Ivanov commanded the Foxtrot-class SS *Magnitogorskiy*, damaged by a well-coordinated attack by the Canadian frigate *Huron* and the American frigate *Truett* on the evening of the 23rd about 200 miles south of the coast of Iceland.

For a while Ivanov managed to evade his attackers. But, unable to snorkel, he was forced to surface several hours later. A Dutch Orion from Keflavik detected the Foxtrot and delivered the coup de grace. An American Sea-Air-Rescue (SAR) team picked up Ivanov and a score of his crew. The captured Soviet commander later told interrogators:

We left the Kola with 20 torpedoes. My first attack was on an American frigate (the John L. Hall). I fired four torpedoes, of which one hit, damaging her. That afternoon, I attacked again, firing a second four-torpedo spread that hit nothing. After evading a counterattack, I did an end run.

Submerged ahead of the convoy, I had an excellent position. I fired a third spread, again of four torpedoes, several of which hit, and sank another frigate (the Nipigon). I now had only four torpedoes left, and I was not about to steam for five days, some 2,000 miles, back to base without a single torpedo.

I had fired a dozen fish in the first twenty-four hours. I used four more torpedoes during the attack that later forced us to the surface.

Captain Ivanov's predicament may have been repeated many times those first two days and may explain why the Soviet effort waned just as it seemed on the verge of success. Of the most modern submarines, the Mike-class only carried twelve torpedoes, and the Akula-class fourteen. With an ideal firing spread of three or four dumb torpedoes, two wire-guided, or single Type-65, the typical Soviet submarine could expect to launch from three to six attacks before having to undertake the long and dangerous journey back to the Kola.

Substitution of surface-to-surface missiles for torpedoes in the initial load of more modern Soviet submarines had little value in convoy attacks.

The Saratoga launches a F-14 Tomcat. The Tomcat, armed with a long-range Phoenix air-to-air missles, controlled by an excellent radar that allowed as many as six targets to be engaged simultaneously, provided American carrier battle groups with protection from Soviet strike bombers such as the Backfire.

Flight Ops on the JFK.

As one Canadian escort commander commented: *You at least had a chance with the missile. You could evade it, fool it, or shoot it. You couldn't shoot the torpedo. And an individual sub couldn't get enough missiles in the air at once to overwhelm you. You could shoot them down. Besides, firing the missile often gave their position away, and some of the older ones had to surface to fire. They didn't like to do that when they knew that our helos or patrol planes might be overhead. No, the torpedo was still the real threat.*

While the convoys battled their way across the North Atlantic on 21 July, significant NATO naval forces began concentrating and moving towards the Norwegian Sea. The Royal Netherlands Navy's ASW Groups I and II, consisting of one destroyer and six frigates, steamed northeast of Scotland. The Royal Navy's Third Flotilla, which included the carriers *Illustrious* and *Invincible*, six destroyers, and six frigates, concentrated in the Orkneys, under cover of RAF Tornados based at Wick. The First and Second Flotillas, several frigates, replenishment ships, amphibious transports (carrying two Royal Marine battalions of the UK-NL AF), and STUFT (Ships Taken Up From Trade) vessels prepared to sail from Rosyth and Holy Loch respectively. (The 800 Dutch Marines of the Amphibious Force flew into Britain late on the 21st and sailed from Rosyth on the morning of the 23rd.)

The most powerful force concentrating in the North Atlantic was the U.S. Navy's Striking Fleet Atlantic (STRIKFLTLANT). Unfortunately, the initial focus on the Mediterranean during the crisis of June and July had diverted forces to the Mediterranean slated for deployment further north. On the morning of 21 July only Carrier Strike Group One (CARSTRIKGRU ONE), the carrier *Coral Sea* with two cruisers (including Aegis cruiser *Valley Forge)* and three destroyers, was anywhere near the Norwegian Sea. It was stationed midway between Iceland and Scotland where its planes could close the gap in air coverage between NATO bases in Iceland and the UK. The "Ageless Warrior," commissioned in 1947, was too small to carry the F-14s considered indispensable for the protection of the battle group from Soviet bombers armed with stand-off missiles. SACLANT considered it too risky to move the *Coral Sea* further north until she was joined by the *Theodore Roosevelt* task force, then steaming northeast about 600 miles west of Reykjavik.

COMSTRIKFLTLANT's Amphibious Striking Force (AMPHIBSTRIKFOR), transporting the Marine Striking Force (MARINESTRIKFOR), over 7,000 Marines of the 6th MEB, was about 100 miles from Reykjavik on the morning of 21 July. It was positioned to reinforce Iceland should the Soviets, to quote COMMARINESTRIKFOR, Lieutenant General Clarence Wunderlin, try a surprise strike at the small NATO nation so critically positioned in the North Atlantic. Two additional carrier task forces were also steaming north to join the *Coral Sea* and *Roosevelt.* The carrier *Saratoga,* accompanied by several cruisers and destroyers as well as the battleship *Iowa,* was about two days behind the *Roosevelt,* hurrying north at over thirty knots. The *John F. Kennedy,* which had passed through the Strait of Gibraltar and entered the Mediterranean early on the 21st, had reversed course and was steaming north.

Until the 21st, the *Kennedy* task force had been under orders to join the Forrestal in the central Mediterranean in support of the planned invasion of Libya. Rear Admiral Terry Kraus, commanding the *Kennedy* task force, wrote: "We had just inchopped to Sixth Fleet when we heard that the war had begun. We received an immediate message to turn about and steam at best speed for the Irish Sea."

Much wrangling had preceded the decision to send the *Kennedy* to the Northern Flank. Under the plans in force, she should have steamed to the North Atlantic to join the Striking Force. Her commitment to the Mediterranean was contingent on the crisis with Libya remaining isolated. On the 20th, as intelligence indicated the likelihood of a Soviet attack, plans were drawn up to move the carrier task force back north. But her proximity to the Mediterranean led Admiral Gerard Gleeson, Commander-in-Chief, U.S. Naval Forces Europe (CINCUSNAVEUR), whose NATO hat was Commander-in-Chief Allied Forces Southern Europe (CINCSOUTH), to propose that if the *Kennedy* had passed the Strait before the Soviet attack, she should remain in the Mediterranean rather than retrace her wake. Rear Admiral Michael P. Schwartz, Head of OP-60, the Navy's Strategic Plans Division later wrote:

There was an obvious rationalty to the idea.

With the Kennedy in the Med, we would have had a nice, comfortable symmetry--three carriers in the Med, three carriers on the Northern Flank. It was a politically comfortable idea. But it wasn't strategy.

Secretary of Defense Powers concurred with Gleeson. CNO Admiral Dunn and SACLANT Admiral Maloney favored shifting *Kennedy* to the north. Word of this split got to the President. When the President asked for more information, Admiral Dunn set up a hasty briefing by Schwartz, "the most significant one of my career."

The post-briefing discussion degenerated into an argument between the Secretary of Defense and the Head, Strategic Plans. Schwartz recalled:

Jim Powers wasn't known as a "strategic heavyweight" in the Pentagon. When the President pressed him on his reasoning, and keep in mind that he was an old Navy man, and an aviator, Powers started pointing out the "choke points" labeled on a map that one of his aides had brought along to make the SECDEF's case. Finally the pointer came to rest on Cape Horn. I couldn't resist the temptation. "Ah," I said, "The Strait of Magellan, a veritable dagger held at the heart of Antarctica!" There was some not so subdued laughter, led by the President. The Chairman just looked the other way. I'd made our case. The President decided that if the Soviets struck before the Kennedy reached Sicily, and there was every indication they would, the carrier would turn and head for the Norwegian Sea.

On the evening of the 23rd, the *Kennedy* reached the Irish Sea, steaming north at over 30 knots.

Within forty-eight hours of the start of the war, NATO had significant naval and amphibious assets heading for the Norwegian Sea. But Soviet forces, including their new carrier, were already operating off the Finnmark coast, and an amphibious task

force bearing three battalions of the 63rd Naval Infantry Brigade was only 300 miles from Narvik. Late in the evening of 22 July, many Soviet and NATO commanders concluded that the reinforcement race had already been decided.

The John F. Kennedy races north to join STRIKFLT.

NATO had lost the battle for the Norwegian Sea, and perhaps the campaign on the Northern Flank.

Flanks Collapse

Turning the Tide

62

Despite the setbacks the Soviets suffered in Finnmark and Lapland during the first 48 hours of the offensive, the situation on the ground looked dismal from the vantage point of AFNORTH headquarters at Kolsas.

In fact, CINCNORTH, General Sir Ian Moore, watched almost helplessly as his flanks teetered on collapse. To the south in Germany and Denmark, COMBALTAP was under heavy pressure. The Second Guards Tank Army had driven to the outskirts of Lubeck and Hamburg and was on the verge of breaking into the Jutland peninsula.

Soviet, East German, and Polish airborne, airmobile, and naval infantry forces were landing throughout Denmark, as *Spetsnaz* units seized or destroyed key bridges and ferries. COMBALTAP had narrowly missed sharing the fate of COMNON when his Danish security force was initially surprised by a *Spetsnaz* detachment that had approached the NATO headquarters at Karup in a fleet of refuse removal trucks. This time, however, the defenders prevailed. The situation in northern Norway, while developing more slowly, seemed

Jet blast deflector in position and catapult ready, F-14 Tomcat at the moment before launch.

critical as well. The Soviet overland drive appeared to be proceeding apace, disrupting Norwegian mobilization throughout the Fydde. Soviet airborne forces held Bodo and were blocking the E-6. When he had learned of the destruction of COMNON headquarters at Reitan, Sir Ian immediately dispatched his deputy and a jury-rigged staff to Bardufoss to take over the defense, but the C-130 carrying them fell victim to a MiG over Narvik.

Command then devolved to Norwegian Lieutenant General Hans Breivik, who commanded a reserve divisional staff at Bardufoss. Breivik, a diligent and able commander who was poorly served by his staff, quickly became overwhelmed by the pace of events.

Recalling those chaotic hours, Bundeswehr Generalmajor Friedrich Heinzen, commander of the Allied Command Europe Mobile Force (ACE MF), who worked with Breivik, wrote:

Breivik and his staff had their hands full just trying to get the individual Norwegian brigades and battalions to act cohesively. His communications were poor. And he had little sense of what was happening outside the immediate area, down at Bodo for example. He had elements of three Norwegian brigades fighting there at one stage of the campaign, but he had no idea of where they were or what they were doing. His headquarters was simply unable to direct a campaign spread across northern Norway, with troops from six nations, with different capabilities, strengths, and weaknesses. To his credit, he recognized this and made little attempt to dictate. Things were chaotic, but we got along fairly well. The real problem that we had up there, and it wasn't Breivik's fault, was poor coordination between the ground and the air. The loss of the COMNON staff may have contributed to the problem; however, those who had experience with the Norwegians, claimed that ground-air cooperation had never been their fort.

What Breivik did comprehend on the evening of 22 July was that the war was not going well, and he made his concerns known to CINCNORTH in several messages that, General Moore said, "smelled of impending disaster."

Apparently, the Soviet blows, predictable as they were, had been effective. The northern airfields were under steady attacks, which made airborne reinforcement increasingly difficult. The E-6 was severed. And until the Soviet Navy could be driven from the Norwegian coast, the immediate movement of reinforcements or supplies by sea was impossible.

To compound matters, the Soviet Northwest Front still had six battalions of the 76th Guards airborne uncommitted. Moreover, if the Soviets did not yet "control" the air, they certainly had demonstrated their ability to make use of it. Intelligence indicated that several Soviet naval infantry battalions were already in transport and would probably attempt a landing somewhere south of Tromso on the 23rd or 24th.

As a result, all of the important Norwegian airfields and ports still needed garrisoning. But Breivik lacked the assets required to protect his position against envelopment from the sea and from the air and simultaneously to hold the Lyngen line against two Soviet corps.

CINCNORTH was sympathetic, but had few reserves to spare. Air transport assets were limited and fully committed to the movement of the 13th Norwegian Brigade to Bardufoss on the 23rd and 24th, a brigade of three battalions deemed insufficient to stop the rot in the north.

Meanwhile, the 14th Brigade was moving up the E-6 from central Norway. COMSONOR also released the 5th Brigade, which was entrained and sent north. But the deteriorating situation in Denmark ruled out any wholesale transfer of Norwegian forces from southern Norway. Moreover, with Soviet paratroopers blocking the E-6 at Rognan, southeast of Bodo, COMNON could expect little immediate assistance to reach him from the south.

Therefore, the only help available had to come from "higher authority." Fortunately, NATO did have plans for such a contingency. In fact, once the situation in the north began to deteriorate, transports carrying the NATO Composite Force for Norway (NCFN), an oversized, multi-national battalion of 2,500 men, were dispatched. They began arriving at northern airfields on the afternoon of the 22nd.

Formed at the prompting of General John Galvin when he had been SACEUR in the late 1980s, the NCFN replaced the Canadian Air Sea Transport (CAST) Brigade, which the Canadian government had decided in 1988 to break up and integrate into its other NATO forces stationed in West Germany.

Penguin-armed USAF F-16 Fighting Falcon. Penguin is a true fire and forget missile, capable of launch from ships, aircraft, or vehicles.

Because of the gravity of the situation, General Moore also wanted the Allied Command Europe Mobile Force (AMF) committed to the Northern Flank. At 1400 on the 22nd, SACEUR agreed.

Shortly thereafter, Generalmajor Friedrich Heinzen got the call at his headquarters in Seckenheim. Within an hour, transports carrying the British 1st Battalion, the Parachute Regiment, the Italian Susa Alpini battalion group, the 1st battalion of the West German 24th Gebirgsjäger Brigade, a company from the Luxembourg 1st Light Infantry battalion, a British armored reconnaissance squadron, and a battery of Italian mountain artillery began departing from airfields in Hesse, Baden, and the Palatinate for Bardufoss, Evenes, and Tromso.

NATO air reinforcements also began arriving in Norway—one Dutch, three American, and seven British squadrons during the first forty-eight hours. But only three of the formations were able to deploy to the northern airfields to join the overworked Norwegian 339 squadron.

Indeed, the increased activity around the northern airfields proved to be too much to handle. A severe bottleneck resulted. Without the ability to keep these airfields operations, air movement of reinforcements into the Norwegian fortress area faltered.

AFNORTH's air deputy summed up the problem well: "It was what you Yanks call, I think, a 'Catch-22.' You see, we couldn't get command of the air unless we could get more fighters to the northern fields, and we couldn't get more fighters to the northern fields unless we could get command of the air."

The arrival of three squadrons in the north helped, but it was not enough. Soviet strikes on the airfields kept coming, greatly diminshing the capacities of the airfields. The additional planes that did get through overtaxed the ground support system. In the end, there was no point bringing in fighters that would be left unserviced, idle, and exposed on damaged runways.

The loss of the field at Bodo crippled NATO's reinforcement efforts. It was strategically placed between the airfields in the north and those further south. In retrospect, it should have been more heavily protected.

By the late evening of 22 July, it had become apparent at Kolsas that whatever assets SACEUR made available for employment in the NEC would probably not get through. The restrictive air corridor to the north would likely force a diversion of the reinforcements to central Norway.

In fact, at 2330, SACEUR made just that suggestion to CINCNORTH. But Sir Ian refused to give up the defense in the north. "The Lyngen position was the best in the NEC, perhaps the best in all of Europe, and I will not surrender it without a fight," he said. So after securing the release of substantial reinforcements from SACEUR, Moore, undaunted, turned to SACLANT for additional assistance.

A journal entry by Moore later shed light on his thinking of that time:

It was becoming obvious to me by the evening of the 22nd that we in the NEC had reached one of those crisis points in operations. I kept going around and around with my staff, looking at the situation in the air and on the ground, and at all the difficulties, all of which were neatly intertwined. And it became evident that the only way to break this knot was with the Striking Fleet. The American carriers could prevent the Soviet amphibious landing. They could open the Norwegian Sea for our use, and we could land our own substantial amphibious forces. The operation of two carrier air wings might swing the balance in the air to our favor. At the minimum, it would take some of the pressure off the airfields. And if we could do that, then we could expedite the movement of air and ground reinforcements to the north. So I turned to my naval staff and asked what was for Americans, I suppose, an often asked question: "Where are the carriers?" Unfortunately, they were not as close as I had hoped. I remember saying, "Why do they call them the fast carriers? They seem to be going about this a bit slow to me." So we called SACLANT to see what could be done.

Admiral Maloney recognized the seriousness of the situation in the NEC, but he faced difficult problems of his own. The opening phase of the war in the Atlantic had not gone as well as many NATO planners had expected. "It wasn't that we were not doing well, it was simply that we had not reached the positions we had hoped to reach before the beginning of hostilities," he later recalled.

American planners had expected to begin the war with a pair of carriers in the Norwegian Sea, but the focus on the Mediterranean between the month of crisis of June and July, compounded by the unwillingness of NATO to move forces north of the G-I-UK Gap before the 21st, ensured that SACLANT would start the war in the hole. As he later testified before Congress:

The lack of political will displayed by NATO on the eve of war was distressing, to say the least, and certainly did retard Allied reinforcement of forward positions. It did not, however, I repeat, not prevent the movement of American carriers north of the (G-I-UK) Gap. The big problem was the buildup in the Med. We had the Coral Sea, but she was over forty years old. While still a valuable asset, as a carrier she proved to be too small to handle the Phoenix-armed F-14 Tomcats that were central to our carrier battle group defensive doctrine. I was unwilling to push her north without another carrier in company. Therefore, she had to wait for the Teddy Roosevelt to come up. Nevertheless, we could have moved air and Marines into Norway. That we were not able to do so, I consider unconscionable. Many men and women paid for that decision with their lives.

To avoid Soviet submarines, the *Theodore Roosevelt* task force and the Amphibious Striking Force had to change course several times during the 21st and 22nd. But a far more important factor in the seemingly tardy approach of the Striking Fleet was its makeup.

A task force is no faster than its slowest ship. American carriers, battleships, cruisers, and destroyers were capable of speeds of over 30 knots. But the accompanying replenishment ships, the amphibious vessels, and the Striking Fleet's flagship, the *Mount Whitney*, were more than 10 knots slower. If the combatants had forged ahead toward the Norwegian Sea, they would have had to leave the slower ships behind. As COMSTRIKFLT Sigal commented:

The subs were a problem, but it was the damn Backfires that troubled us the most. People have it all wrong when they call the ships that accompany a carrier her "escorts." It's the other way around. The carriers escort the other ships. When you realize that, you can understand the problem. My carriers had to escort my supplies and my Marines. There was no point in getting to the Norwegian Sea if the Backfires swept in behind me and got my tankers, ammo ships, and amphibs. So we spent the first two days heading for the Gap at about 20 knots. Another problem involved the prevailing winds, which blew from the southwest. To launch and recover we had to steam away from the Norwegian Sea. That posed a constant aggravation throughout the campaign.

By the evening of 22 July, the *Theodore Roosevelt* and the amphibious group made its rendezvous with the *Coral Sea* task force about 200 miles northeast of the Faroes, still 600 miles short of Narvik. At 2345 Sigal received a message from SACLANT.

"It was basically a 'what can you do and when can you do it' dispatch," Sigal later recalled. He was not surprised. His staff had monitored the situation throughout the 22nd and had expected "the call" from Kolsas. "We had already determined that, at our present rate of advance, we wouldn't be able to do anything effectively on the 23rd."

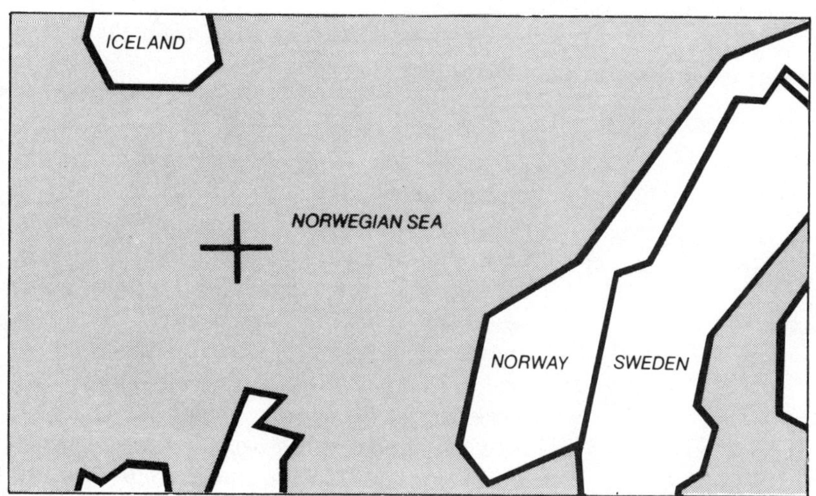

Positions of American carriers, 22-23 July. Slow speed of cargo and amphibious vessels limited task force's move northward.

Within minutes of receiving the signal from SACLANT, Sigal had his response on the way to Norfolk: STRIKFLT would either have to cut loose from the slower ships or Moore would have to carry on for another day. Sigal added a request that he be allowed to communicate directly with CINCNORTH, rather than continue to pass messages through Norfolk. SACLANT agreed.

"I could see that a major decision was coming and Marc, who was on the scene, could best judge the situation. Sitting back in Norfolk, I wasn't about to tell him how to dispose of his ships," SACLANT later recounted.

Before contacting Moore, Sigal called together the STRIKFLT, AMPHIBSTRIKFOR, and the MARINESTRIKFOR staffs.

I laid it all out. We could continue to move north at the present rate, but the campaign might be lost in the meantime. Or we could cut the carriers loose, but that meant risking our replenishment ships and, most importantly, the amphibs—and the Marines they carried, of course. My staff had figured out that we could run the amphibs to the southeast, toward Trondheim, where they would come under CAP from Orland in about sixteen hours. And even after we split up, we would be able to cover them for about six to eight hours. They could then move north along the coast. The replenishment ships would follow the carriers, solo, unprotected. The route we would be taking seemed to be clear of submarines. Hopefully, individual ships would escape detection. I, and about half of my staff, would transfer to the TR. The Mount Whitney would stay with the amphibious group. That would mean degraded coms, but if that meant less traffic from Norfolk and Washington, so much the better. We would be moving north under strict EMCON (emissions control) in any case. My intell people had a Russian satellite going over us then, at the same time some heavy cloud cover was moving in from the west. If we waited about two hours and then broke, hopefully the Russians would focus on the carriers' projected path and miss the other ships.

We had it all laid out on this big chart. Hank (Lieutenant General Wunderlin) just kept staring at it, saying nothing. We kept looking at his staff, but they just looked at him and were not about to say a word until he spoke. Finally he looked up at me. "Ten hours is a hell of a long time up here without air cover. But I guess it's worth it if we can get you off this ship and have it to ourselves. See you in the Vest Fiord."

Sigal ordered the immediate transfer of a skeleton staff to the *Theodore Roosevelt.* He called Moore at AFNORTH and promised support before day's end. His last message from the Mount Whitney went to SACLANT, informing Admiral Maloney of the decision.

The risks COMSTRIKFLT ran by dividing his force and leaving portions of it without air cover became apparent on the morning of 22 July. The

Soviet long range Backfire bombers were a threat to the divided task force.

tempo of Soviet anti-shipping operations suddenly increased, and the complacency that had developed among some NATO commanders during the first forty-eight hours of the war, when the SNA had been most notable for its absence, quickly disappeared.

Late on the evening of 22 July, Northwest Front released SNA and AADS assets for operations in the Norwegian Sea and North Atlantic. The 45th and 54th Corps broke Norwegian and Finnish resistance along the borders and required little air support for the two to four days it would take them to reach the Lyngen position.

Meanwhile, NATO air activity slackened noticeably. Few transports reached the heavily damaged northern airfields during the 22nd. Although the Soviet strikes had failed to destroy the Norwegian airbases, there seemed little point in continuing to suffer the steady loss of aircraft to the Norwegians' newly installed and highly effective NASAMS.

The Norwegian Advanced Surface-to-Air Missile Systems, which had replaced the older HAWK batteries, relied on state-of-the-art three-dimensional radar controlling ground-launched AIM-120A advanced medium-range air-to-air missiles (AMRAAMs). The Soviets soon learned that the American-made system, to which the Norwegians had added numerous dummy launchers and bogus radars, were difficult to destroy or suppress.

Sweeps by AADS MiG-25s and MiG-31s reached

KNL Falcon patrols, like this pair over a Norwegian fiord, broke up Soviet air landing forces.

into the Norwegian Sea, well south of Trondheim, contesting control of the air throughout the day against American F-15s, Norwegian F-16s, and UK-based RAF Tornados.

The fierce air battle forced NATO and American AWACS to patrol further south, beyond the reach of the aggressive Soviet fighters. Meanwhile, under the cover of these operations, Badgers mined Trondheim harbor, while Soviet reconnaissance aircraft sought to locate and track NATO surface forces. Additionally, individual Tu-95 Bears flew deep into the North Atlantic, searching for convoys steaming beyond air cover.

These missions met with mixed success. One Bear was picked up by AWACS and downed by

a Keflavik-based F-15 off the east coast of Iceland. Two Badgers that approached the Striking Fleet were destroyed by F-14s flying from the *Theodore Roosevelt*. But a Kola-based Bear that had escaped detection by flying between Greenland and Iceland located a small American convoy about 250 miles east of Cape Farewell. The Tu-95 managed to track the American ships, without itself being detected, for over two hours. At 0415 the SPS-52 radar of the frigate *Kaufman* picked up a dozen contacts approaching from the north at about 150 miles. Backfires, flying from Olenegorsk, had followed the path of the Bear. Based on data provided by its Big Bulge radar, they launched about twenty ASMs at a range of

100 miles, well beyond the 20-mile range of the American frigate's SM1MR SAMs. Fortunately, several of the incoming Soviet missiles malfunctioned. For its part, the *Kaufman* managed to down two with SAMs and two more with her Mk 30, 127mm gun. The ammunition ship *Mount Baker's* Mk 15 Vulcan Phalanx downed another.

But four hit the frigate, sinking her in minutes, and one hit the *Mount Baker*, causing severe damage that slowed her speed to 8 knots. The submarine tender *Emory S. Land* escaped unharmed. Unfortunately, at 1145 a second wave of attackers finished off the small convoy, sinking the *Emory S. Land* and the damaged *Mount Baker*.

The loss of the *Emory S. Land* severely crippled the American submarine effort in the Northeastern Atlantic. It meant that American submarines had to retire to Scotland to replenish their torpedoes, rather than to Tromso where SACLANT had intended to establish a forward operating base.

Meanwhile, 200 miles west of Trondheim, the Royal Navy's Third Squadron was detected by a Bear escorted by MiG-25s. A pair of Harriers

USAF F-15 Eagle firing a deadly AMRAAM missile. F-15s operating from Iceland and Norway, along with RAF Tornados from Scotland and Norway, played central roles in maintaining control of the air during the campaign.

dispatched from the carrier *Illustrious* were caught by surprise and downed by the Foxbats. Before help could reach the British force from Orland, ten Backfires and a Tu-16 Badger A ESM (electronic support measures) aircraft, covered by fifteen Foxhounds, began their attack approach.

Soviet Backfire bomber carrying an AS-4 anti-ship missile. During the course of the campaign, Backfires proved to be a deadly threat to NATO surface ships operating without air cover.

Another Harrier was lost in a futile interception effort. About 200 miles out, the Backfires released their missiles. Of the thirty Kingfishes launched, all but two were downed (many of them by the Harriers), diverted by electronic countermeasures or chaff. Others simply malfunctioned.

One Kingfish, however, with its 1,000 kilogram warhead, hit the frigate *Scylla*, which was transformed into a flaming wreck which sank in thirty-two minutes. Another struck the frigate *Broadsword* but failed to explode. Fortunately, having been fired at extreme range, the missile had little unexpended fuel. The subsequent fire was extinguished by the ship's crew. The *Broadsword* remained operational. Though slowed down, she was able to keep up the 15-knot speed of the amphibious and replenishment vessels steaming with the British squadron.

Orland-based RAF Phantoms reached the scene too late to prevent the attack, but soon enough to draw blood. The American-built fighters downed a pair of Foxhounds, the Badger, and three Backfires, for the loss of a single Phantom.

Farther north, Norwegian Falcons from Bardufoss surprised the Soviets and destroyed another MiG-31 and four Backfires. This attack prompted Northwest Front to reassess the previous day's decision to divert its effort away from the northern airfields. Since photo-reconnaissance during the afternoon of the 23rd indicated that transport aircraft were arriving at the northern airfields, Northwest Front promptly ordered the resumption of the air campaign against the bases. Soviet anti-shipping attacks on 23 July demonstrated that operating without air cover within range of Soviet land-based aircraft was extremely hazardous for NATO naval forces. Additionally, small carriers, like those of the Royal Navy, were not platforms capable of providing the airborne early warning (AEW) and the combat air patrols that the dispersed ships of a modern naval task force required. Had the Soviets repeated the attacks of the morning of 23 July, there might have been little left of the British squadron.

Sea Battle

Operation Northern Trident

It became increasingly evident during the 23rd that a critical, and perhaps decisive, battle was shaping up off the northern Norwegian coast. Thirty-eight Soviet combatant, amphibious, and replenishment ships, as well as a half-dozen submarines, had already rounded the North Cape. The approach of NATO reinforcements heralded a major clash, the largest naval battle since the end of the Second World War.

The prospect of coordinating such an engagement from his KPF in the Kola troubled Admiral Alexis Khomiakov, CINC of the Soviet Northern Fleet. The shortcomings of Soviet command and control methods had become evident during the first two days of the war. Showing his concern, at 2330 on the 22nd, Khomiakov ordered a third KUG of two cruisers and three destroyers to steam from Murmansk.

Vice-Admiral Maxim Kramskoy, Khomiakov's deputy, flew his flag in the command Light Cruiser *Zhdanov*. After joining the Soviet forces already in the Norwegian Sea, the *Zhdanov* served as a Flag Command Post (FKP) coordinating the

Soviet warships replenish under way in the Norwegian Sea. The Soviet Navy lagged behind NATO in at-sea replenishment capability.

operations of the various Soviet groups. Kramskoy's arrival brought to twenty-six the number of major Soviet surface combatants in the Norwegian Sea.

While few NATO surface ships were available to challenge the advance of the Soviet armada on the morning of 23 July, beneath the waves, a concentration of nuclear attack submarines assembled by COMSUBEASTLANT during the 21st and 22nd lay in wait. The Royal Navy SSNs *Spartan*, *Talant*, *Trafalgar*, *Superb*, and *Conqueror*, and the American *Whale* and *Tunny*, had formed a patrol line running from the Troms coast NNE for about 300 miles. CINCNORTH had also instructed the Norwegian diesel submarine *Kunna*, operating in the fiords, to work under Vice Admiral Weir's command.

Throughout the morning and afternoon of the 23rd, Weir's submarines engaged the Soviets as they steamed south. NATO submariners, sensing the importance of their mission, pressed their attacks. By evening, the cruisers *Zozulya*, *Kronstadt*, *Varyag*, and *Nakimov*, the destroyers *Krasnyy Krym*, *Ukrainyy*, and *Gnevnyy*, and the frigate

Svirepyy, had been sunk. In comparison, NATO losses were light. The *Kunna* had been sunk and the *Whale* damaged, both by Soviet surface forces. The failure of the six Soviet submarines in the Norwegian Sea to assist the surface forces effectively during the 23rd earned harsh reprimands for the few commanders who survived the campaign. But Captain Second Rank Pavel Savelev, who commanded an Akula-class SSN and escaped to the west after the war, wrote that the fault lay not with the submariners, but with "the surface officers who succumbed to panic."

The NATO submarines were right in among our surface ships, which were spread throughout the entire northern Norwegian Sea. The acoustics were terrible. It rained most of the day and the noise of so many ships made sonar detection difficult. I was unable to form any kind of overall picture of the situation. Every time I came near the surface to extend an antenna and attempt communication, to provide the KPF with a position report, I was driven down by air attack--by our own helicopters! I was attacked eight times in fourteen hours. Frankly, I think the presence of our submarines that day aided the enemy effort, and I said as much at my court of enquiry. But it was not because we submariners were ineffective, it was because the surface ships wasted so much time hunting us, that they had that much less time to hunt the enemy. We diluted their efforts.

By late afternoon, the *Zhdanov* was only 100 miles from the *Tblisi*. Kramskoy established communication links with the surface strike, ASW, and amphibious groups in the Norwegian Sea. But the loss of ship after ship to NATO submarines and the confusing, contradictory reports from Soviet commanders convinced Vice-Admiral Kramskoy the situation was already out of control.

Of particular concern to Kramskoy and the

FKP staff was the location of the Striking Fleet's carriers. At 1410 the *Tblisi's* Flankers drove off a poorly executed, weak strike by American carrier planes. The KPF intelligence staff at Severomorsk cited the very weakness of the attack as evidence that the carriers were still far off, concluding that the restrictions posed by the need for aerial refueling had limited the size of the strike force.

But Kramskoy was not convinced. Since an 0140 satellite pass, no firm position report on the American carriers had been received. The staffs at Severomorsk and on the *Zhdanov* had plots on their charts and computer displays that showed the estimated position of the carriers based on their last reported course and speed—twenty knots.

Soviet reconnaissance planes had either failed to locate the carriers or were shot down in the attempt. The heavy cloud cover, typical at that time of year, hid ships from overflying photographic satellites. And jamming, or some other kind of interference, had left Soviet radar and infrared satellites temporarily inoperative.

At 1706, minutes after Khomiakov passed operational control to Kramskoy, the latter informed Severomorsk that he intended to retire to the north until the American carriers were located. At 1713, Khomiakov suddenly resumed operational control and countermanded Kramskoy's orders.

At 1722, the FKP ordered the Soviet surface groups to move into Norwegian waters and use the fiords to cover their movement from enemy submarines. Kramskoy protested. The fiords offered protection from submarines, but would prove to be deathtraps in the event of air attack.

Only after the war did Kramskoy learn that the orders had come not from Admiral Khomiakov, but from the Northwest Front commander, General

Mikhail Kovalesky, whose principal concern was the planned amphibious landing. "To Kovalesky," one high-ranking Soviet naval officer later wrote, "the ships and brave men of the Northern Fleet were expendable."

While the Soviet surface forces sparred with COMSUBEASTLANT's attack submarines, CARSTRIKGRU ONE steamed northeast at over thirty knots. The 1400 strike, a hastily arranged affair, had been mounted to support a KNL-RAF strike from Orland. Unfortunately, the diversion of British and Norwegian fighters to the air battle in central Norway forced the last minute cancellation of the attack. But the decision, made by the COMSONOR Air Staff at Oslo, reached COMSTRIKFLT too late.

An enraged Vice Admiral Sigal later recalled:

We lost some good men, several planes, and valuable ordnance. I was damn sure not going to do that again. I told the Strike Ops guys to work on the assumption that when we struck, we would have no help. They were to work in contingencies for outside coordination, but the plans were to be set up so that we could execute the attack on our own if necessary.

About 1800 Sigal learned that the Soviets were heading for the Norwegian coast, either to land their forces north of Tromso, or to seek shelter in the fiords from the NATO submarine attacks. The reports "made my day," Sigal later remarked.

A Soviet amphibious landing north of Tromso posed no risk to the NATO left flank in Fortress Norway. And if the Soviets expected to continue to work their way through the fiords, their slowed passage south would give Sigal additional time to close the range and prepare his attacks.

Sigal, who had served previously as a carrier group commander and a carrier CO, had gained firsthand experience in the Norwegian fiords during NATO exercises, so he understood well the advantages and disadvantages inherent in such operations.

Clearly, fiords provided a degree of protection for surface ships from submarine attack. Submerged navigation in the fiords was dangerous because sonar effectiveness was reduced and approaches were limited, so they were more easily patrolled and defended.

Fiords also offered defensive advantages against missile attacks, since many were sheltered by offshore islands. Surface ships positioned between these islands and the coast could hide from enemy surface radar. Even in the absence of intervening terrain, the high fiord walls, rising from the sea to heights of over 3,000 feet, offered a backdrop that made it difficult for an ASM's or SSM's seeking radar to pick out targets.

On the other hand, there were also disadvantages to operating in fiords. The same poor acoustics that degraded the sonar of submarines also adversely affected defending helicopters and surface ships. Moreover, maneuver, especially in the foggy morning hours, was dangerous. The effectiveness of defensive SAM systems was also reduced because the fiord walls created blind zones for surface radars. Finally, carrier air operations were more difficult, and in some cases impossible, depending on the direction of currents and winds.

Despite these problems, American naval officers had long considered feasible the establishment of "Carrier Havens" in the fiords to seek safety from Soviet submarine and air attack.

For his part, Vice-Admiral Kramskoy understood that the fiords did not offer his ships the same degree of protection afforded NATO men-of-war. Unlike the Soviets, the Americans relied principally on their carrier aircraft, not their SAM systems,

Soviet Helix helicopter. Modified Helixes, pressed into an airborne early warning role, proved far inferior to the U.S. Navy's E-2C Hawkeyes.

for air defense. While the Soviets possessed great numbers of long-range SAMs, they would be of little use against attacks launched from land. In a confined Norwegian fiord, it was often easier to bomb a ship than to hit it with a long-range standoff missile. Soviet anti-shipping strike aircraft relied almost exclusively on missiles and had virtually no capability to bomb American men of war. American and NATO strike aircraft, on the other hand, carried shorter-range missiles, such as the Harpoon and the Penguin, as well as a variety of "Smart" bombs, precision-guided-munitions (PGMs) such as the laser guided Rockeye II.

In NATO exercises in the fiords, friendly forces controlled the coast. American Marines operated ashore with radar and communication equipment tied to the battlegroup and provided the extended radar view otherwise denied ships by fiord walls, while American carrier-based E-2C Hawkeyes provided long-range airborne early warning.

As the Soviet surface groups moved south into the fiords on 23 July, NATO forces, predictably, controlled the coast. Moreover, the modified Ka-27 Helixs flying from the *Tblisi* proved to be ineffective airborne early warning platforms compared with the Hawkeyes.

When Vice Admiral Sigal learned that the Soviets had entered the fiords, he immediately had visions of the British ships in the Falklands, stuck in the Sound, as Argentine planes swooped in over the hills, getting on top of the Brits before they had a chance to react. In Sigal's view, COM-SUBEASTLANT's attacks had driven the Russians into a death trap. And now, it was now his job to spring it. Sigal made a note to send Weir a case of Scotch the first chance he got.

As the *Coral Sea* and the *Theodore Roosevelt* steamed northeast at 32 knots, the Strike Ops Staff of Carrier Group One completed its plan—Operation NORTHERN TRIDENT. The plan had two phases:

PHASE I: As EA-6B Prowlers, ESM aircraft, jammed communications between the Soviet fighters and their controllers, F-14s and F/A-18s would intercept the Flankers and Forgers flying CAP over the

Steam vents from catapult as the Coral Sea launches an F/A-18 Hornet.

Soviet surface groups and clear the skies for the follow-on attack aircraft.

PHASE II: After the fighters were airborne, the *Coral Sea* and *Theodore Roosevelt* would launch pairs of Intruders and Hornets throughout the evening. These planes would overfly the Norwegian coast and begin their attack runs from the east, guided to their targets by Hawkeyes monitoring the battle. HARM-armed A-6 Intruders would assist the strikes by knocking out Soviet search and fire-control radars. Additional fighters and Prowlers would launch and relieve the initial wave to maintain steady pressure on Soviet defenses.

The primary target for the Navy attackers was the *Tblisi.* Commander Michael "Moose" Simmonds, who headed the Strike Ops staff, wrote:

If we could get that carrier, and knock out their CAP, we could do what we wanted with the other ships. It wasn't just that they were in the fiords. You have to realize that their ship-based SAMs were just naval versions of their land-based SAMs. The Israelis dealt successfully with them in Syria. And we flew right through them in Libya. We were confident we could beat them. SAMs are not wonder weapons. They may raise the costs of conducting strike missions. But they do not prevent a determined enemy from executing his mission.

After sinking or crippling the Soviet carrier, the NATO attackers then planned to go for the ten Soviet amphibious ships and attempt to sink them before they could land their three battalions of naval infantry. After that, all enemy ships would be fair game.

COMSTRIKFLT communicated the basics of the plan to CINCNORTH, SACLANT, and COMNAVEASTLANT, especially the routes to be traversed over Norway by carrier attack aircraft. In his message, Sigal recommended areas of

F-14 Tomcat getting a "cat-shot" from the Theodore Roosevelt catapult, accelerating from zero to 140 knots in less than three seconds.

operations and the timing of subsequent strikes should the commands commit assets to support the CARSTRIKGRU ONE effort. In any event, the attack would begin at 1900, whether such support was forthcoming or not.

At 1803 the *Coral Sea* and *Theodore Roosevelt* began launching their planes. The *Theodore Roosevelt's* group consisted of a pair of Tomcats, eight Hornets, and a Prowler. The *Coral Sea's* group, also led by a pair of Tomcats from the *Theodore Roosevelt*, included nine Hornets and a Prowler.

Unlike the Americans, who had to maintain CAPs at great distance to intercept Russian bombers armed with ASMs with ranges of up to 250 miles, the Soviets, knowing that the best American standoff ASM was the Harpoon, with a range of 80 miles, were able to maintain a tighter, and more efficient CAP at a 100-mile radius from the *Tblisi*.

The leading Tomcats were 200 miles from the *Tblisi* when they picked up approaching Flankers. Once the Soviet interceptors were within seventy-five miles of the American planes, the Tomcats fired four Phoenixs each. Six of the sixteen American missiles found their mark; and the effort to avoid the missiles also broke up other Soviet formations. The Tomcats, still armed with Sidewinders and Sparrows, stood off to protect the Prowlers while the Hornets closed in and engaged the Flankers in a dogfight.

The Russian pilots were heavily outnumbered in the air. During the course of the battle, the *Tblisi* managed to launch another dozen Flankers to join the dozen already airborne when the American attack began.

But the twenty-three American fighters of the initial wave were soon joined by eleven RAF Tornados and nine KNL Falcons leading a strike of Buccaneers from Orland. Within thirty minutes, the battle in the outer air defense zone had been decided.

NATO fighters then closed in on the *Tblisi* where the Forgers, joined by a few surviving or late-launched Flankers, formed an inner air defense zone. The superior NATO fighters made quick work of the Forgers.

Lieutenant David "Spud" Marsh of VFA-131, the Wildcats, flew a Hornet from the *Coral Sea.*

The Hawkeye had tracked the Flankers all the way. As soon as the range looked good, the Tomcats released their Phoenix missiles. These had the desired effect, downing several of the Flankers and breaking up quite a few of the Russian formations. At about thirty-five miles out, we engaged the Soviets with our AMRAAMs. Each Hornet carried a pair. More Flankers went down. At about twenty miles out, the Soviets were finally able to respond and let loose some Alamos, their AMRAAMs. It was one of these that got Jerry (Lieutenant Gerald Ramsey), my section leader, and damaged my radio. And, I'll admit, seeing

Soviet Su-27 Flanker. The Flankers proved to be worthy adversaries of the best NATO fighters. Not as highly maneuverable as some NATO aircraft and the MiG-29 Fulcrum, the Flanker had an effective radar and carried all-aspect AA-8 Aphid, and AA-10 Alamo fire and forget air-to-air missiles.

his plane disintegrate right in front of me shook me up bad.

Things then just became a mad furball—worse than anything I had ever seen at Top Gun or Fallon. And I just wasn't with it. Before I knew it there was a Flanker on my tail and I was maneuvering for my life. The next thing I knew, I was at about 700 feet, right over the water, and the sky was clear—not a plane to be seen.

I was trying to get the radio to work when four blips appeared on my screen: two to port and two to starboard. My first thought was to hightail it out of there, but then suddenly one of those little "rules" you pick up along the way during your career popped into my head: "the best move—defensively or offensively—is an aggressive move."

I figured if I turned, they would be all over me. So I flew right at them and waited for them to make their move. As we closed I began to get the feeling that they didn't know where I was. I was low and I figured they didn't see me. So I kept closing the range. At about ten miles I got indications of weak radar emissions from them and all of a sudden it dawned on me—they were Forgers. I continued to close. At about seven miles, I began a gentle climb. I was about 3,000 feet below them.

I fired a Sparrow at the lead Forger to port, and three seconds later another at his wingman. The first hit and the plane disintegrated. The second one missed.

I flew right between the two elements; and I still didn't think they knew just where I was. I went to afterburner and pulled the stick back, intending to come up and get behind them. But they had sighted me and the starboard element began turning hard right to get around behind me.

We passed head-to-head a second time. I banked right and pulled, while they did a Split S. I fired a Sidewinder, but it missed. We passed head-to-head again. I had another shot, but it dawned on me that I had fired three of my six missiles and had only hit one plane—I had three more to go, so I decided to cool down and work for a better shot.

As we passed, I saw the third plane veer in front of me. I tore off after him, but he picked me up and began to turn to port. The other two were now going hard to starboard to get around behind me for a heatseeker shot. I broke off my pursuit, banked hard right and dove, turning well inside the Forgers. I could see them out of the top of my canopy. They seemed to hesitate, unsure of whether they should bank left or right.

By the time they went right, I was coming around, climbing up under them. Boy, I'll tell you, those Yaks were D-O-Gs. They couldn't VIFF (vector in forward flight) like our Harriers. Anyway, I had the missile shot, but I was pulling lead and held on until I had closed to within cannon range. The deflection was pretty bad, but I got him. I was below him when I took the shot. I think the section leader was unsure just where I was. He banked left, the wrong way, and brought his plane right across my HUD. I fired a Sidewinder and it got him.

I then banked left, looking for that last Gomer and found him. I lit the afterburner and in about two minutes was within missile range. He must have been green. He just flew on, straight ahead. I pulled in right behind and below him and pitched the nose up a bit and downed him with the cannon. No chute. I turned for home. The whole dogfight had taken about seven minutes.

Before the last of the Flankers and Forgers had been driven from the sky by the NATO fighters, Hawkeyes began directing attack planes from the two American carriers towards the *Tblisi.* A pair of Intruders from the *Theodore Roosevelt's*

A Yak-38 Forger. The Forger was slow, unmaneuverable, had limited range, and carried obsolescent missiles. It proved far inferior to the Anglo-American Harrier V/STOL aircraft.

VA-35 Black Panthers initiated the attack, but were downed during the run in on the *Tblisi.* Two A-6s from the *Coral Sea's* VA-55 Warhorses were luckier. Lieutenant Commander William Van Camp led the strike.

We were following a valley which led into the Malangen Fiord where the Tblisi had holed up as her CAP was destroyed. It went pretty smooth. The biggest scare came when we turned a bend and almost ran into some high tension lines that, I guess, had gone up after our charts had been prepared. It was real close.

We entered the fiord as some other planes were attacking. We came out of the valley at about 500 feet and had a direct approach to the carrier. We were already too close for a SAM. Soviet attention seemed riveted on the other attackers. We saw them go down. The Russians fired their ADMG 630 (the Soviet version of the Vulcan Phalanx) and put up a real wall of lead. My wingman went down. We finally entered "the basket," the area where you could attack with a laser-guided-bomb, painted the target, and began to pull up.

We released five Rockeye IIs, cluster bombs, and held the lock continuing to pull up until we heard explosions. I think all five hit. Looked like it pretty much messed her up topside. The fire control radars must have been knocked out because we didn't come under any fire from the carrier as we pulled away. I went low, trying to keep the Tblisi between me and the other ships for protection. We flew up another valley and headed back inland.

For the next forty minutes, Navy Intruders and Hornets launched attack after attack, usually in pairs, against the lone Soviet carrier. By 1945 hours, she was burning out of control.

Simultaneously, RAF Buccaneers and KNL Falcons began attacking the Soviet amphibious transports. After the demise of the *Tblisi* was assured, Hawkeyes directed American attack planes against the transports as well. Nine of the ten ships were soon sunk and over 2,000 Soviet naval infantrymen were lost. Only one heavily damaged Alligator-class amphibious ship managed to reach Andoy, landing about 150

An American A-6 Intruder returns from a strike on the Tblisi. This design, more than thirty years old, proved itself one of the most versatile strike planes of the war. Its sturdy airframe, combined with continually upgraded avionics, gave it longevity.

shaken survivors of a battalion of the Kirkenes Brigade near Dvarberg.

With the *Tblisi* sunk and the Soviet amphibious group destroyed, Northwest Front returned operational control to Vitse-Admiral Kramskoy who immediately ordered the remaining Soviet surface groups to retire to the north. But this time, they would have to run the gauntlet without air cover, thanks to the poor judgement of General Kovalesky. In the end, it was Khomiakov who paid for this miscalculation.

Kramskoy's ships might have succumbed to the same fate were it not for Vice Admiral Sigal's decision in the early morning of 24 July to turn south to cover the approach of the AMPHIBSTRIKFOR and the replenishment ships *Seattle* and *Milwaukee*.

"I was sorely tempted to maintain the pursuit and complete the victory," Sigal later wrote, "but my actions were determined by logistics and the risks further movement north entailed for the Marines."

Throughout the 24th, NATO air attacks nevertheless continued. Ground-based aircraft—RAF Buccaneers and Harpoon-armed Nimrods, similarly armed American Orions, and Norwegian Falcons—sank three Soviet cruisers, three destroyers, and three replenishment ships, and damaged the cruiser *Kursk*.

Soon thereafter, the *Frunze* fell victim to Harpoon-armed B-52s of the USAF 42d Bomb Wing. Major Mike "Bullwinkle" Paul flew one of two "Buffs" from Loring AFB in Maine toward the Norwegian Sea.

We were guided by a Sentry (AWACS) until he turned us over to a Navy Hawkeye. We came in on a high profile. The weather guys had given us a good forecast with two big airmasses coming together right near the coast. By flying high we

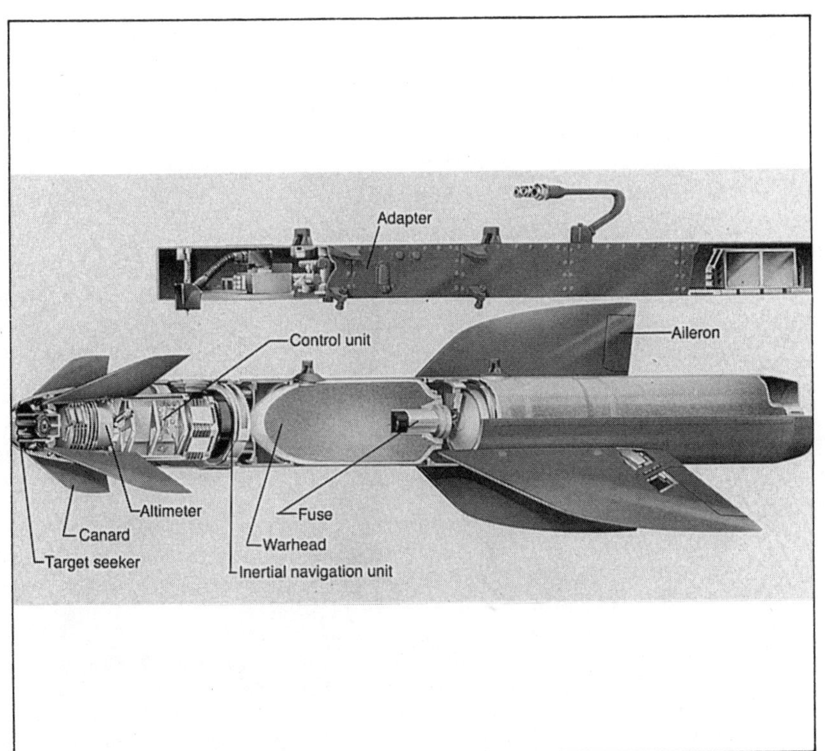

hid over this duct, while the Hawkeye served as our eyes. Then we went low for the final run in. About sixty miles out, we each launched a pair of Harpoons. We got the word from the Hawkeye as we banked away for home that all four hit. We sent a message to Loring as soon as we heard: "The Moose is Loose!"

Norwegian anti-ship attacks against Soviet vessels in the fiords made the most of terrain and equipment.

Only on the morning of 25 July, when Kola-based fighters were able to provide cover, were Kramskoy's ships able to retire safely to Pechenga to begin repairs and to replenish expended ordnance and stores.

During three days of intense fighting, both the Soviets and NATO had suffered heavy losses. The Soviet Northern Fleet lost forty vessels,

USAF-USN cooperation. Navy F-14 Tomcats escort Air Force B-52 after the strike that damaged the Frunze.

including fifteen submarines. AADS, SNA, and LMD aircraft losses totaled about 125. NATO, for its part, lost thirty-seven ships, eight of them submarines, and eighty aircraft, about a fourth of which were from the American carriers.

But the rough equivalence in losses, cited by Soviet historians and analysts to support their claim of a drawn battle, did little to hide the obvious: by late evening, 24 July, NATO had won the Battle of the Norwegian Sea. The Soviets were retiring and NATO succeeded at opening the SLOCs into northern Norway. Soon, NATO amphibious reinforcements were able to land in the Vest Fiord, where three Soviet Black Death battalions had been destroyed, save for the small

force that had scrambled ashore at Andoy.

Moreover, among the thirty-seven NATO ships sunk were a dozen relatively expendable Norwegian fast attack boats. The Soviet Northern Fleet, on the other hand, lost the new carrier *Tblisi* and the damaged battlecruiser *Frunze.* Half of the thirty Soviet submarines available to contest NATO control of the North Atlantic between the G-I-UK Gap and the Barents Sea were lost—in three days! Several others were damaged and many more were at sea, but out of torpedoes.

In the Norwegian Sea, CAP from the American carriers prevented the Soviets from using their air assets to prosecute the submarine war, so outnumbered Soviet submarines faced air, surface, and subsurface threats, while NATO submarines faced only the subsurface threat (and, of course, the occasional mistaken attack by friendly forces).

The presence of nearly 100 naval fighters, Tomcats and Hornets, also tilted the air balance in NATO's favor and gave the Norwegian airfields a needed respite which was used to repair runways and support facilities, and to turn around the increasing number of transport aircraft moving Norwegian and NATO reinforcements into northern Norway.

Between 23 and 26 July, major NATO reinforcements reached northern Norway. By the 24th, lead elements of the Norwegian 14th Brigade moving north up the E-6 collided with the 2nd battalion of the 234th Guards Airborne Brigade at Rognan. The Soviet paratroopers, outnumbered and without their heavy equipment, were driven back across the Saltelv River into Finneid.

The Norwegian attacks continued on the 25th and 26th. In heavy fighting, the 14th Brigade, now reinforced by advance elements from the 5th, pushed a battalion of the 239 "Danzig" Guards Brigade out of Finneid and seized the junction of the Bodo road and the E-6. The 2nd Battalion of the 15th Brigade, which had mobilized at Narvik, probed south along the E-6 before being halted by Soviet paratroopers north of Fauske.

As the assaults on the 76th Guards intensified, the Soviets strained their air transport resources to fly the division's heavy equipment into the airhead. But operations from the two American carriers and the related recovery of the northern Norwegian airfields made the Soviet effort more difficult.

Late on the 24th, a squadron of Soviet transports overflew neutral Sweden. Stockholm protested, but failed to take any measures to halt the flights. The Soviets continued to circumvent NATO air patrols throughout the 25th, ignoring repeated Swedish protests.

On the morning of 26 July, a pair of RAF Tornados downed four Soviet Candid transports over Sweden. By way of explanation, NATO informed the Swedish government that if it could not defend its own airspace, NATO aircraft would. The next Soviet transport mission was intercepted and turned back by Swedish fighters which downed one recalcitrant Candid. Subsequently, NATO provided AWACS data to Swedish fighters in the north.

South of Bodo, near Trondheim in central Norway, USAF MAC transports carrying the men of the 4th Marine Expeditionary Brigade began landing at Vaernes. The Marines "married up" with their equipment and were soon moving north by road and helicopter.

Of more immediate concern at COMNON and AFNORTH was the movement of the 13th Norwegian Brigade, the NCFN battalion, and the ACE Mobile Force to northern airfields. Soviet air activity had forced the cancellation of many of these missions during the morning and afternoon of the 23rd.

But with the arrival of the American carriers in the Norwegian Sea, the situation improved dramatically and the transports began reaching the northern Norwegian airfields without incident late by the 23rd and throughout the 24th.

The men of the 13th Brigade, after taking their prepositioned equipment out of storage, took up positions along the E-6 north of Bardufoss. "Fritz" Heinzen's ACE Mobile Force backed up the 13th Brigade and took up positions along the Finnish-Norwegian border astride the E-78.

On 25 July, NATO amphibious reinforcements also began to reach northern Norway. The AMPHIBSTRIKFOR landed advance elements of the 6th MEB at Harstad in the And Fiord—to which the ships of MPS I had been directed as they reached the Norwegian Sea. Transport aircraft ferried additional personnel of the MEB from the United States to the nearby airfield at Evenes. The Royal Marine's 42 Commando unit landed at Korsnes, a critical ferry point, along the coast south of Narvik, while 45 Commando unit remained afloat.

NATO reinforcements had arrived none too soon. By the evening of 26 July, lead elements of the Soviet 118th Brigade of the 54th Corps reached the Norwegian Border along the E-78. But British paratroopers were there in time to bring the Soviet headlong advance to an abrupt halt. In response, Northwest Front ordered the 54th Corps to delay further attacks. Meanwhile, elements of the 45th Corps had just reached Kvaenangsbotn where the E-6 bends around the Kvaenangen Fiord, still forty miles short of NATO positions.

By 26 July, the situation on the Northern Flank had improved dramatically for NATO. The Soviet fleet had been swept from the Norwegian Sea, and Russian submarines were being rolled back toward their bases in the Kola. The SLOCs were open, and Fortress Norway, "Island" Norway, could now be supplied by sea.

NATO maritime superiority and the arrival of highly mobile amphibious forces suddenly made the timely reinforcement of threatened NATO positions possible. It also provided the means for a NATO counterattack against the rear of the Soviet advance as it continued south. In the air, NATO also seemed to be gaining the upper hand. This meant that transports bearing reinforcements could get through. Not surprisingly, at AFNORTH, the mood had shifted from one of defeat to guarded optimism.

Nevertheless, while Soviet plans had thus far been foiled, the campaign was by no means over. In fact, the principal Soviet ground forces—the 45th and 54th Corps—had yet to be engaged in decisive action, let alone defeated.

How would the NATO troops hold up in the face of attacks by the tired, but tested, Soviet tank and motorized rifle battalions? The E-6 was still blocked and Bodo would attract the attention of significant NATO forces for several days.

While the Soviet Northern Fleet had failed to prevent the movement of NATO surface forces into the Norwegian Sea, significant SNA and AADS air assets still remained, and might yet destroy or drive off the NATO armada and deny the alliance the use of the SLOCs. General Sir Ian Moore wrote in his diary late on 26 July:

Things certainly seem to be going our way. We've got the upper hand in the air and at sea. We're getting our reinforcements into the north. But what dispositions are being made? What is the mood of the troops, especially the Norwegians? I am still very much concerned about the command situation at COMNON. It's not clear at all just who is running the show up there and communications are not what I would like. If the situation in Denmark wasn't so bad, I would fly to Bardufoss myself.

The Soviet attack will begin soon, perhaps tomorrow. I have done all I can from here. I keep trying to impress upon everyone that despite our advantages, we still have to defeat the Red Army if we are to win. That will require some hard fighting.

Seizing the Initiative

Soviets in Tromso

Despite the naval setbacks suffered by the Soviets in the Norwegian Sea during the 23rd and 24th of July, optimism remained high at Northwest Front forward headquarters at Murmansk. Colonel Vorontsev, the Stavka staff officer detached to the Northwest Front, remembered:

Despite all of the Marxist-Leninist rhetoric, higher Soviet staffs reflected an "Army," rather than a purely "joint," mentality and view. The Navy had suffered defeats, but many of us had long considered the Navy's building program a waste of precious resources. The Air Force, operating independently, had not achieved the desired results, but we believed that its performance would improve once it got down to basics—supporting the Army's advance.

We, and I say we because quite honestly I too shared the view, felt that our Army had yet to weigh in. We believed that when the troops came into contact with the enemy, our tactics and weapons would sweep the NATO forces aside. We had reports from Germany that our units had not been able to maintain the expected rate of advance, but nowhere had our forces been stopped in their tracks. We only had to push 100 miles to break the so-called Fortress Norway position. Certainly we could drive that far.

But Soviet optimism was more tempered at the headquarters of the 45th and 54th Corps. Nearly a week on the poor Arctic roads of Norway and Finland had taken its toll on men and machines.

Lieutenant General Matvei Liashchenko, 54th Corps commander wrote:

I visited the forward units of the 118th Brigade on the afternoon of the 26th. I talked to one battalion commander who told me that his men had been on the move for six days, and had averaged an advance of fifty miles a day. But the men were filthy and exhausted and seemed unmoved by my visit. They looked more like a defeated than a conquering army. The zampolits (political officers) were not much better. They maintained an optimistic front, but I could tell they were just waiting for me to leave so that they could get some sleep.

Supply also posed problems. Ammunition stocks were high, for few of the units had been in combat, but fuel consumption had exceeded expectations, so shortages were common by the 27th. Major Afanasii Shaklovity, who later conducted a logistical study of the campaign for the General Staff, attributed the problem to poor planning. Soviet logisticians had assumed that their vehicles would motor their way to Fortress Norway in high gear, getting good gas mileage. But harassment by Finnish and Norwegian troops along the roads, including mining, fallen trees, and blown bridges, and the breakdown of Soviet vehicles often slowed the columns and forced drivers to stay in low gear.

Higher than expected fuel consumption led to the depletion of reserves well ahead of schedule, and supplies could not be moved forward along the crowded roads. One commander of a tank company of the 54th Corps recalled being forced to halt his tanks for five hours on the 24th, while still in Finnish Lapland, until helicopters brought additional fuel forward.

At 1900 on 26 July, Lieutenant Generals Bagdasarian (45th Corps) and Liashchenko (54th Corps) met with Colonel General Dimitrii Pokrovsky at the forward headquarters of the Soviet Sixth Army at Kautokeino, Norway. Both corps commanders had doubts about the offensive that was to begin the following morning.

Neither commander was happy with the plan drawn up by Northwest Front. Since the 45th Corps was behind schedule, front headquarters ordered the 54th Corps to attack alone on the 27th. A troubled Liashchenko, who had only a single brigade on hand, believed that his assault should be delayed an additional twenty-four hours so he could rest his men and bring up additional forces, supplies, and heavy equipment. Underlying both commanders' fears were the lessons of history. "Tannenberg," Bagdasarian recalled, "was on our minds and we did not want to become the Rennenkampf and Samsonov of the Third World War."

While numerous western historians interpreted the reluctance of the 45th and 54th corps commanders to begin the attack on 27 July as evidence of their opposition to any further offensive moves on the ground in northern Norway, in fact, both Bagdasarian and Liashchenko were determined to press forward. "It was a question of when, not if," Bagdasarian wrote. "We had not come so far only to give up and retreat without a fight just because the Navy had lost a few ships."

Bagdasarian and Liashchenko found Pokrovsky sympathetic. Pokrovsky had moved his headquarters forward into Norway earlier in the day, and he, too, was troubled by what he saw as he neared the front.

In a dispatch to Northwest Front commander General Kovalesky, Pokrovsky "suggested" alterations in the Northwest Front plan and forwarded the requests of Bagdasarian and Liashchenko for permission to use chemical weapons to support the offensive.

The "Kautokeino Message" caused a tempest at Northwest Front headquarters. Kovalesky was disturbed by the lack of confidence displayed by his subordinates. According to Colonel Vorontsev's recollection:

During the course of the campaign, I traveled often to the front and met with Bagdasarian and Liashchenko. They were good, solid commanders. But it became clear to me that they totally dominated Pokrovsky and held little respect for General Kovalesky. Kovalesky had, it is true, risen quickly to high command, having played a role in the ouster of Gorbachev. He was seen at the front as a political general. He was . . . I think you have a term in the United States . . . a "desk puke." Bagdasarian and Liashchenko had both fought in Afghanistan and they had, as the latter put it to me one evening, "been forced to cut through the shit of Marxist-Leninist dogma and doctrine to try to find some way to carry out the mission and keep their people alive."

Nevertheless, Kovalesky remained determined to attack as planned. Intelligence indicated that NATO ground and air reinforcements were moving into northern Norway so every hour's delay allowed COMNON to improve his position. Kovalesky also understood that the Soviets were losing the reinforcement race. The overall plan for the offensive, of which Bagdasarian and Liashchenko had only seen the parts assigned

F-14 Tomcat launch, from deck level. F-14 kills depleted air support for Soviet ground offensive.

to their respective corps, called for a three-stage assault.

At 0200 on 27 July, the 54th Corps would attack out of the Finnish Wedge along the E-78. At 2200, the 45th Corps would strike overland from Kvaenangsbotn to Vinnelys, along the new E-6 extension that followed the north shore of the

Lyngen Fiord, and simultaneously across the Fiord near the old E-6 ferry at Lyngseidet.

Kovalesky hoped that the 54th Corps' attack would force COMNON to commit reserves inland which Soviet air attacks could then pin down, opening the way for the advance of the 45th Corps and the Front's airmobile elements. By the 28th, the airmobile LMD Brigade would be in position to attack Tromso island. Kovalesky had briefed Pokrovsky on this plan and its rationale before he departed for Kautokeino, but Pokrovsky raised none of the objections voiced by his two corps commanders.

Apart from the plan of maneuver, the request from Kautokeino for authority to use chemical weapons also caused consternation at Northwest Front headquarters. While Kovalesky understood the position of his corps commanders and the attractiveness of chemical weapons as a means to maximize the shock of the initial attack, he was certain his subordinates knew that such authority would not be granted.

Six days into what had thus far been a non-nuclear, non-chemical conflict, the GKO, which had turned down earlier requests from commanders in Germany, was unlikely to initiate use of such weapons to gain advantage in the mountains of Norway.

To the Northwest front staff, the request appeared to be an effort by Bagdasarian and Liashchenko to protect themselves should the offensive fail. "If things went wrong," Colonel Vorontsev remarked, "they would be able to claim that it was the fault of whoever had denied them use of chemicals."

Soviet leaders had weighed the political and military advantages and disadvantages at an 18 July GKO meeting and had concluded that use of chemicals would likely prove counterproductive. As Western defense analysts had correctly predicted in the late 1980s, the Soviet army had shifted its doctrine from an integrated nuclear-chemical-conventional offensive to a conventional-only theater offensive.

Not surprisingly, no permission to use chemical weapons was forthcoming. Nor was the plan of maneuver for the offensive of 27 July altered by Northwest Front. In fact, the only tangible outcome of the Kautokeino meeting was the shattering of any confidence that had existed between the commanders at the front and Kovalesky back in Murmansk.

At 0200 on the 27th the 118th Brigade of the 54th Corps began its attack out of the Finnish Wedge. The 1st battalion of the brigade attacked along the E-78 but was stopped dead in its tracks by the British Paras. Meanwhile, the 2nd and 3rd battalions, leaving their BMPs behind, struck at the Norwegian Chief of Defense battalion which had taken up positions in the mountains just inside the Finnish border.

These positions, however, proved more difficult to hold. In fact, the Soviet attack, well supported by artillery, helicopter, and air units, steadily pushed back the Norwegian defenders. By the end of the day, Soviet Army troops had raised the Soviet flag on Mounts Kahperusvaare (4,000 feet) and Reisduoddarhaldde (4,245 feet) after driving the CHOD battalion back across the border.

At 1900 the 61st Brigade of the 45th Corps collided with the 1st battalion of the Norwegian 15th Brigade along the Reisa River. But the uncoordinated assault was easily repulsed, resulting in heavy Soviet losses.

The Soviet plan of attack had called for two of the 61st Brigade's battalions to move overland without their vehicles, while a third followed an old track that led to a fordable point along the river. But the Norwegians had mined the track, which the Soviets only discovered when one of the column's lead vehicles, carrying the battalion's detachment from the Commandant's Service—the "Map Reading Corps"—exploded.

Subsequently, a simple "navigation" error

committed by a junior officer who, like so many other Soviet officers, could not read a map, led the column down the wrong track and into a dead end. Seizing a moment of opportunity, six KNL Falcons struck the stalled battalion and all but eliminated it as a fighting entity. The task was an easy one for the Falcons since the AADS fighters that were supposed to cover the Su-17 ground attack aircraft assigned to support the 61st Brigade's assault, never materialized. Apparently, American F/A-18 Hornets from the *Coral Sea* had shot down four of the Fitters and drove off the rest.

The 45th Corps attack across the Lyngen Fiord also failed, mainly because the Corps assets were still stretched out along the E-6. To compound matters further, a battalion of the 10th Brigade had to be diverted to block two Norwegian battalions holed up on the peninsula between the Porsangen and Alta fiords. But once contact was made the Norwegians withdrew and took up defensive positions at Kvalsund which overlooked the crossing to Kvalšy Island and the port

A tank-mounted scissors bridge of the Soviet 45th Corps 61st Brigade ferries across a Norwegian river.

of Hammerfest. Moreover, only advance elements of the Soviet 253rd Brigade arrived in time for the Lyngen assault, spelling doom for the 45th Corps' plan.

Apparently, a company of infantry from the 253rd, which were lifted by helicopter across the fiord south of the ferry point, had been spotted by a Norwegian observation post on Mount Jaeggeyarre, at 6,000 feet. The sentry alerted Major Anders Bildt who commanded the reserve battalion group from Alta. Bildt responded immediately.

I had read that during the Second World War, once the Soviets were allowed to establish a bridgehead, they were impossible to dislodge. So I left a single platoon to guard the ferry and led the rest of the battalion to the Soviet lodgement. I asked for some air support and got a pair of RAF Harriers. They drove off the Soviet attack helos and bombed and strafed the Russian positions. We attacked and in a three-hour battle destroyed the bridgehead and took over 100 prisoners.

Reports of Bildt's success reached COMNON headquarters at Bardufoss as NATO's ground force commanders met for the first time. Lieutenant Generals Breivik (COMNON), and Wunderlin (II MEF), Generalmajor Heinzen (ACE MF), and Brigadier General James Fitzgerald, Royal Marines (UK-NL AF), gathered to discuss how best to employ the reinforcing formations that were reaching the northern flank.

To the NATO commanders, the situation along the front appeared stable. Norwegian troops had held firm throughout the day on the left and in the center. And Soviet success in the mountains along the Finnish-Norwegian border posed little immediate threat to the right flank. Meanwhile, three battalions of Heinzen's ACE MF and the NCFN battalion had taken up positions along the front line in support of the Norwegians. For the moment at least, Fortress Norway seemed secure. The next question involved the American, British, and Dutch Marines. Breivik expected continued Soviet attacks and wanted additional reinforcements fed into the front lines to buttress the defense. He envisioned moving from the defense to the offense: after blunting Soviet assaults, his forces would counterattack and drive the Russians back. But Wunderlin, who controlled not only his own Marines but also Fitzgerald's (which had been chopped to STRIKFLT), opposed the commitment of Marine battalions into the Fortress area. According to Brigadier General Fitzgerald's recollection of the meeting:

Hank (Wunderlin) was in a tizzy. He was already upset by SACLANT's decision to go along with CINCNORTH's request that control of 4 MEB remain with COMNON until the E-6 was reopened and Bodo retaken. The prospect of seeing his Marines fed into the Fortress region sent him up the wall. I believe he thought Breivik was a bit dim. He certainly was limited in his vision of the battlefield.

Wunderlin, for his part, had an entirely different conception of operations. He felt that sufficient forces were already committed to the defense of the Lyngen position. The American, British, and Dutch Marines, with their amphibious and airmobile capability, could best be used to strike at the Soviet's right flank. Wunderlin later commented:

Breivik, like most of the Norwegians, saw things along a north-south axis so to speak. Their lives were linked to the damned E-6. They just looked up the road and down the road. I saw things from a different perspective. I looked east-west—from the sea to the Norwegian coast. Here were the Russians, hundreds of miles from home, with their lifeline running back along one stinking road, laid out along the coast. Hell, God created Norway for the United States Marine Corps, no two ways about it. I could strike anywhere along that road and grab the Russians by the balls. And here was Breivik telling me that good generalship was sending my men into the mountains to throw themselves in front of Russian attacks. That was bull.

As I saw it, the Marines were the reserves for the campaign; we were money in the bank. And Breivik was in a hurry to spend us. I wasn't. We were still getting 6 MEB outfitted and concentrated. The Dutch hadn't caught up with the Brits yet. And I wasn't particularly concerned about what happened with COMNON. The further south the Russians drove, and the deeper they were engaged, the better.

As for Bodo, I expected the Russians to destroy the runways, so we would get little use out of the base. The Norwegian forces down there could have turned the place into a POW camp for the Russian paratroopers. We wouldn't even have had to feed them. I told Breivik: "Hey, you don't have to worry about recapturing airfields, I brought two along with me and another two are on their way." That's what the carriers are all about.

Heinzen didn't share Breivik's concerns for the security of the Lyngen position either. The German commander, whose father had fought with the 3rd Mountain Division at Narvik in 1940, wrote in his memoirs: "Breivik was concerned that if we were forced back, our retreat would become a rout under the pressure of the Soviet pursuit; I did not believe that such a pursuit, in the terrain of north Norway, was possible."

Fitzgerald, who shared Wunderlin's views, but was also eager to see the Royal Marines engaged, suggested a compromise, proposing that 42 Commando move south by helicopter and join

4 MEB and the Norwegians in an accelerated assault on Bodo that would break the Soviet position quickly and free the American Marines.

As the debate continued, Breivik received a message that the airbase at Andoya was now under attack from Soviet naval infantry. Resupplied by air during the 27th, the 150 survivors of the ill-fated Soviet amphibious assault were peppering the airfield with mortar fire and appeared to be concentrating for an assault on the Norwegian garrison.

In light of this new development, Wunderlin agreed to Breivik's request that 6 MEB secure the airbase and round up the Soviets. And although the II MEF commander "had grave doubts about committing even more troops to Bodo," he nevertheless accepted Fitzgerald's suggestion that 42 Commando move south to assist the attack on Bodo. It proved to be, he later wrote, his "biggest mistake of the campaign."

These NATO movements were well under way by the morning of the 28th when four Soviet airmobile battalions of the LMD Brigade began landing on Tromso Island. By day's end the Soviet force had destroyed the defending battalion of Brigade North and seized the town of Tromso, the airfield, and the naval base at Olavsvern, unhinging NATO's left flank and raising the specter of a renewed threat from the sea.

Breivik, visibly shaken by the news, and still upset by the confrontation with Wunderlin the previous night, now ordered a retreat toward Bardufoss. The only reserve at hand, 45 Commando, Royal Marines, was hardly strong enough to take on the entire LMD Brigade. And the American Marines were just beginning their attack on the Soviet naval infantry on Andoy. Given his predicament, Breivik believed that he had little choice but to pull back his left to cover the E-6 from Bardu north. The only way to get enough troops to accomplish this was through a retrograde movement from his center and right.

Heinzen disagreed. "The position was difficult," he said, "but there were only four Soviet battalions. They could threaten us everywhere, but they couldn't actually be everywhere." Heinzen proposed that the NATO forces remain in their positions and wait to see how the Soviets would exploit their success.

But Breivik was determined to retreat, so he ordered his Norwegians to begin moving back, with or without the NATO troops. Heinzen had little choice but to go along.

"I did manage," Heinzen said, "to slow our retreat as much as possible and to ensure that we left nothing behind for the Russians."

While the NATO forces were retreating in the north, 6 MEB rounded up the Soviet's "Black Death" on Andoy. Meanwhile, farther south, Norwegians, American Marines, and the Royal Marines of 42 Commando continued to close in on Bodo. By the 28th they were only twenty miles from the town. But in spite of this progress, a Soviet battalion at Sorfoldt, where the old E-6 ferry crossed the fiord, and another entrenched along the new E-6 extension to the east, continued to put up stiff resistance to Norwegian attacks.

By the 29th, two battalions of 4 MEB joined a pair of Norwegian battalions from the 14th and 5th Brigades in a concentric assault against the Soviet paratroopers in and west of Sorfoldt. After two days of heavy fighting, the Soviet Guardsmen from the 234th Brigade were destroyed. Over 400 prisoners were taken. The E-6 was at last opened. Simultaneously, British, Norwegian, and American attacks drove to within ten miles of the airfield at Bodo, close enough to bring Soviet positions under artillery fire.

Soviet Mi-8 Hip-E attack helicopters support the advance. Flexible 12.7mm nose gun is augmented with rocket packs and Swatter antitank missiles.

At Sixth Army headquarters at Kautokeino, the impending fall of Bodo made the rapid advance by the 45th and 54th Corps seem imperative. If Fortress Norway could not be stormed before the ten NATO battalions engaged around Bodo moved north, the prospects of Soviet victory would be nil.

Since the 54th Corps still had only a single brigade—three battalions and some supporting troops—forward, Kovalesky decided to assign the E-6 and primary responsibility for the continued advance to the 45th Corps. The bloodied 61st Brigade of the 45th Corps would continue its overland advance along the axis Vinnelys-

Grumman A-6 Intruder on final approach to landing aboard its floating air base. Its big ordnance load and sensors made A-6 a versatile attack aircraft.

Birtavarre-Skibotn-Kvesmenes. The 10th and 253rd Brigades would secure the ferry crossing at Lyngseidet and move south along the old E-6.

The 54th Corps would then drive along the E-78 as far as Helligskogen and move south, overland through the mountainous country that lay between the E-6 and the Swedish border.

The LMD Brigade, less the battalion holding Tromso, would move three battalions to the mainland and drive along the road that joined the island to the E-6 at Nordkjosbotn. This four-pronged offensive would hopefully entrap and destroy the defending NATO forces before they could withdraw to the south.

But the unexpected NATO retreat that began on 28 July, in combination with difficult terrain and fatigue, made it impossible for Sixth Army to maintain pressure on COMNON's forces. On the 29th, however, the 54th Corps's 118th Brigade mauled a Norwegian battalion from the 13th Brigade in the mountains along the Swedish border and reached the outskirts of Rosta before being halted and driven back with heavy losses the following day by the West German Gebirgsjäger battalion of Heinzen's ACE Mobile Force, supported by a squadron of RAF Jaguars.

Simultaneously, on the left flank, a heliborne battalion of 6 MEB made a direct assault on Tromso airfield while 45 Commando staged a small amphibious landing on the island. Although the movement of the British transports through the fiords had been delayed by early morning fog, Brigadier General Frederick Jennings, 6 MEB commander, launched his attack on schedule at 0545. He expected the fog to cover his own approach and add an element of surprise to his assault.

But unfortunately, many of the Brigade's CH-46 Sea Knight helicopters lost their way, so Marines ended up being scattered about the southern half of the island. And, as these small groups closed in on the airfield, the Soviet defenders counter-attacked and inflicted heavy casualties on the Marines. Once the fog lifted, however, a dozen Harriers arrived to provide desperately needed ground support. The airfield was taken at 1020. Fifty minutes before, 45 Commando landed on the northern coast and quickly seized the bridge linking the island to the mainland. By noon, Tromso was secure.

For some reason, Soviet air support was conspicuously absent during the fighting at Tromso and Rosta. But NATO pilots, who suddenly seemed to have the skies over Fortress Norway to themselves were not complaining. Generalmajor Heinzen later wrote:

At a commander's conference called by Breivik at Bardufoss late on the 30th, I stated that the situation in the air was the best I had seen since I had reached Norway. Everyone agreed. But we all knew that the turn of events could prove temporary. Everything depended on the outcome of the battle that had been raging in the Barents Sea for the last forty-eight hours.

Turning Point

Strike the Kola

After COMSTRIKFLT's decision on 24 July not to pursue the retiring surface forces of the Soviet Northern Fleet, CARSTRIKFOR cruised to an area between 100 and 200 miles west of Narvik, codenamed Delta Station. Under cover provided by the American carriers, the Striking Fleet's replenishment vessels and amphibious forces, as well as the Royal Navy's carrier, surface, amphibious, and supply ships concentrated safely in the northern Norwegian Sea. Transports flew reinforcements and supplies into the northern airfields, which were enjoying a respite from the incessant Soviet attacks of the first seventy-two hours of the war. Runways were repaired. Sortie rates rose. And, additional squadrons staged forward from central Norwegian bases.

But to the men of CARSTRIKGRU ONE, Delta Station quickly became known as Daffy Station. According to Spud Marsh, "the whole time we were there we felt like sitting ducks." Indeed, CARSTRIKGRU ONE found itself tethered to Fortress Norway. "We were like a big dog chained in a yard," Vice Admiral Sigal commented, "and nasty neighbors stood just outside the radius of our chain throwing rocks; we kept dodging, but we were getting a little tired."

Early on the 24th, satellite imagery revealed the position of the American carriers to the Soviets. That morning, two dozen Badgers, escorted by a similar number of Foxbats and Flankers, mounted the first of many attacks on the *Coral Sea* and *Theodore Roosevelt.* But Tomcats, assisted by Marine Hornets and Phantoms flying from Andoya, after receiving ample warning from AWACS and the carriers' own Hawkeyes, intercepted and drove off the attackers.

Nevertheless, the Soviet strikes continued throughout the day. By early evening, several Badgers managed to penetrate the American air defense zone deeply enough to launch standoff missiles. Fortunately, SM-2ER missiles from the Aegis-class ships *Valley Forge*, *Normandy*, and *Arleigh Burke* were able to destroy the incoming missiles. The defensive strength of the American CVBGs was being demonstrated at a high cost to the Soviets. Thirty aircraft, including twenty Badgers, had been lost. NATO losses, on the other hand, were light, totaling but four planes.

Vice Admiral Sigal was ecstatic:

We had foreseen the possibility of an initial defensive phase during which we would be subjected to heavy and repeated Soviet air strikes. We called this the "Turkey Shoot" phase, a reference to the Battle of the Philippine Sea of 1944 when the Japanese destroyed their land- and carrier-based air power by launching what proved to be futile attacks against American carrier task groups. We expected the Russians to do the same. Then we would hold the initiative and could contemplate further action, perhaps even raids against the Kola itself.

Admiral Khomiakov, having already lost the

A pair of Soviet Badger bombers over the Norwegian Sea. Although antiquated, the Badgers nevertheless proved themselves effective strike planes against surface targets without air cover.

bulk of his fleet, was not eager to throw away his remaining air assets. The Northern Fleet commander ordered the attacks halted.

But Northwest Front commander General Kovalesky demanded that the Navy find some way to drive the American carriers from the Norwegian Sea, no matter the cost. As an alternative to the resumption of costly attempts to penetrate the American air defense zones with large forces, the Northern Fleet planning staff suggested that feints and small strikes be launched in order to keep the American carriers on constant alert and ultimately exhaust the American crews, paving the way for a massed attack that would overwhelm the tired defenders and secure the victory Northwest Front sought.

Beginning on the morning of 25 July, attack aircraft destined for any target in northern Norway followed tracks that appeared to take them directly toward Delta Station. But, at the last moment, Soviet strike planes would change course and proceed to their actual destinations. Additionally, bogus raiders were sent toward the carrier groups

A Soviet MiG-25. The Foxbat is fast, unmaneuverable, and has little capability against low-flying targets. Poor pilot visibility makes the MiG-25 an appalling dogfighter.

only to abort and return to Kola bases.

The constant warnings kept the carriers busy launching additional planes to reinforce their CAP. By the evening of 25 July, the new Soviet tactics appeared to be succeeding. Pilots and the flightdeck crew were exhausted. The number of operational planes declined. While only two planes were lost, the four Soviet aircraft downed that day could hardly be considered victims of a "Turkey Shoot."

At 2230 on 25 July, Vice Admiral Sigal received a backchannel message from CNO Dunn in Washington. It said that the Joint Chiefs were alarmed at the CASREPs (casualty reports) from the Striking Fleet. Because of their concern, a

new directive was issued ordering the *John F. Kennedy* to join the Carrier Striking Force early on the 26th, followed by the *Saratoga* the next morning. These two carriers would then be designated Carrier Strike Group Two and would relieve the *Coral Sea* and *Theodore Roosevelt* which would retire to the south.

At 2400 on the 25th, Rear Admiral Terry Kraus on the *John F. Kennedy* received a message from the Joint Chiefs designating him COMCARSTRIKGRU TWO. Early the next morning he took a chopper to the *Roosevelt* to meet with Vice Admiral Sigal. At an 0900 briefing, Sigal outlined the planned relief of CARSTRIKGRU ONE on the 27th.

"I could see that they were all tired," Kraus

recalled, "they were worn out by the constant attacks. In fact, they had to beat off a raid while I was there."

Once the attack had subsided, Kraus's briefing continued. The improved situation ashore was outlined. And the obvious ability of a CVBG to defend itself was documented. Kraus listened intently until all the briefers had finished their presentations.

"Marc (Sigal) looked at me and said, 'Any questions, Terry?'

"'No sir,' I replied.

"'Good,' he said 'Now, that's what we've been *ordered* to do. What I intend to do is to go up to the Kola and take out Russian air at the source. I'm afraid the Russians are reading our mail, still living off that Walker shit, so I'm not taking any chances with this. I've sent my COS (chief of Staff) back to CONUS to outline the plan for SACLANT and the JCS in person. If CINCEASTLANT and CINCNORTH go along, I think we have a go.'"

Sigal's staff had worked out a detailed plan for a four-carrier attack on the Soviets' Kola bases. To COMSTRIKFLTLANT the logic of the situation was simple.

We had sat up there in the Norwegian Sea for three days with two carriers and taken everything they had thrown at us. We sure as hell could move a little farther north with four carriers and defend ourselves just as well, if not better. If we cut loose like we had on the 23rd and got the right weather—heavy cloud cover—we could slip the Russians again. And it was a generally accepted principle of war that you don't destroy an enemy air force in the air; you destroy it on the ground. We had talked about going up against the Kola for over forty years. The moment was right. We had four carriers. Our northern airfields were in better shape and sortie rates were rising. Reinforcements were reaching the airbases. And I believed that an aggressive move against the Kola would attract such attention that our attack would take pressure off the air situation over northern Norway and carry the air battle farther north.

Kraus was excited at the prospect of attacking the Kola, a concept he had long supported:

I had always used the Hornet's Nest analogy. You find a nest in a tree behind your house and the hornets sting your kids and ruin your barbecues. So what do you do? You can sit out there in the yard with a can of spray and as the little buggers come near you or your kids you can zap them. But you'll never get rid of the problem. If you go right to the source, and smoke the nest and destroy it, you get rid of the hornets for good.

Kraus offered his full support to Vice Admiral Sigal and proposed that he fly himself to Kolsas and Northwood to sketch the plan for General Moore and CINCEASTLANT, Admiral Sir Richard Gough. Sigal agreed.

Kraus was soon on his way to AFNORTH, where General Moore embraced the plan and promised full support. Kraus then flew on to Northwood where he found that Admiral Gough's staff had been drawing up a similar proposal. The cooperation of the Royal Navy's Third Squadron was assured.

Sigal himself flew to northern Norway to meet with the senior commanders ashore.

I took the COD airplane to Bardufoss and met with Breivik, Heinzen, Wunderlin, Fitzgerald, and (Brigadier General Robert) Miller, the American Air Force commander. I explained my intentions to them and they all seemed to grasp the implications. It was also clear to me that the northern commanders looked to Hank Wunderlin for direction. He had

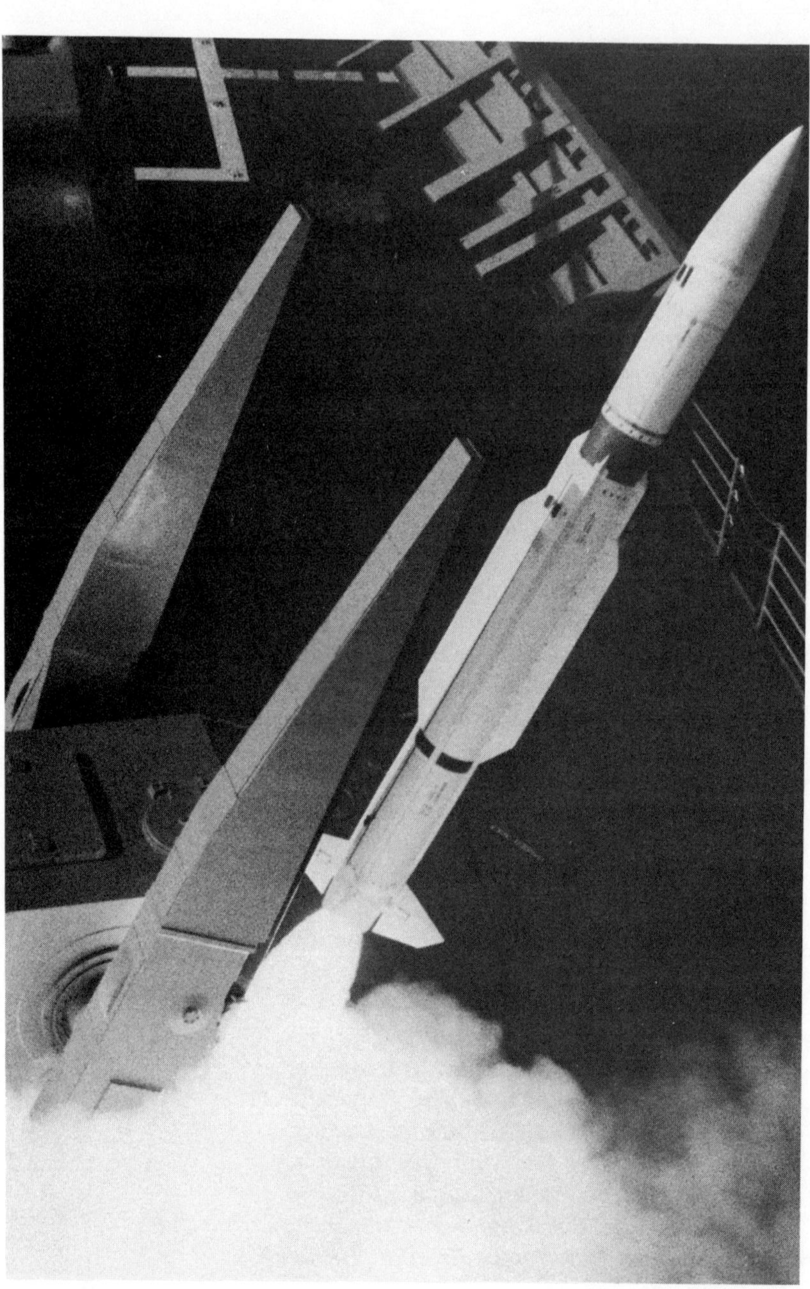

it all—his own army, his own ships, his own helicopters, and his own air force. Hank convinced everybody, especially the Norwegian, that we could take the carriers into the Barents Sea without the Russians regaining the upper hand in the air over northern Norway. Hank had well over 100 aircraft in Norway, more planes than the Norwegian Air Force. He had forty Harriers, over thirty Hornets and Phantoms, a dozen Intruders, and a variety of other planes, all of them, except for some Harriers operating from makeshift bases around Bodo, in the north. And it was clearly becoming an American show. Miller had five squadrons, another 100 aircraft. His planes were mostly in central Norway but were being transferred north as the COB airfields recovered from the early Russian attacks. They had an F-16 squadron at Evenes, and were doing fantastic work with their tankers. Let's face it. We were calling the shots.

Back in the United States, Admiral Maloney continued to trust what had thus far been the excellent judgment of his principal subordinate. CNO Dunn, likewise, proved to be a forceful and effective advocate for the offensive scheme among the Joint Chiefs. By the late evening of 26 July, all the key players were on board. Operation GOLDEN TALON would begin on 29 July.

Despite much of what has been written since the end of the war, to Vice Admiral Sigal and other senior American and NATO officers there was nothing either "daring" or "provocative" about going against the Kola.

Prewar discussion of the Kola option had often portrayed such an attack as so provocative that it could weaken deterrence and perhaps even spark a nuclear conflagration. There had been much speculation that in the event of war the president would not even allow American strikes

The Aegis-cruiser Valley Forge fires a Standard-2 surface-to-air missile during the Soviet attack on 24 July. In combination with the Hawkeye-Tomcat air umbrella, the Aegis system's multiple sensors provided American commanders with excellent pictures of the air and surface situations.

against Soviet territory. But by 28 July, that whole issue had become moot.

At a symposium sponsored by the United States Naval Institute, Vice Admiral Sigal recalled his reasoning at the time:

First, NATO doctrine called for us to strike Kola bases if practicable. Sure, NATO's CONMAROPS was classified, but you didn't have to be in the know, a spy, or a genius to figure out what was going to happen. Even General Hackett's fictional World War III history written back in the late '70s had NATO strike planes hitting Soviet bases in the Kola. We couldn't conceivably fight a successful naval war and treat all Soviet territory as a sanctuary. And even if you could construct some scenario for the northern flank where we avoided striking directly at the Soviet Union, what were we going to do in the Pacific?

Were we just to sit back and allow the Russians to plaster the airfields and ports of our Japanese ally from bases in the Maritime Provinces, the Kuriles, and Kamchatka—all Soviet territory? Do you think the Japanese were going to sit there and take it without striking back at Soviet bases? There was no way it could be done. And we all knew it. I knew as I steamed north on 21 July that the first American attack on Soviet territory would not come from my forces, but from CINCPACFLT. They hit Petropavlovsk that afternoon. There wasn't any debate; it was in the plans and it had been since the late 1940s!

Sigal was right. In fact, the U.S. Navy had begun preparing to conduct operations against Soviet bases in the Northeastern Atlantic in the spring of 1946. As early as the fall of 1949, NATO had adopted "attack at source" as its concept of maritime operations and discussed strikes on the Kola. And the Soviets, not surprisingly, had spent four decades and billions of rubles preparing to

The AWACS version of the Soviet Il-76, the mainstay. Although superior to the old Moss, the Mainstay was not as effective as the American/NATO E-3A AWACS, and may even be inferior to the much smaller Navy E-2C Hawkeye.

defend the peninsula from such attacks.

But despite the impressive Soviet defense effort, NATO planners did not view the Kola as an impregnable fortress. While there were two strategic nuclear submarine bases, two strategic nuclear bomber bases, two strategic early warning and target acquisition radar complexes, over seventy SAM complexes, one theater nuclear missile launch complex, seven submarine bases, nine surface force bases, twenty-two major airbases with hardened shelters and long runways, eighteen minor military airfields, and a variety of command and support facilities throughout the peninsula, there were also chinks in the Kola's armor, weaknesses specifically targeted by the planners of Sigal's Strike Ops staff.

The keys to modern air defense are early warning and effective control of defending forces. No matter how many SAM sites dotted the Kola landscape, no matter how many fighters were based on Kola airfields, warning and control were essential, especially for the Soviets.

The difficulty Soviet ground controllers had

demonstrated during their effort to vector intercepting fighters into an attack position against the ill-fated *KAL-007* airliner, shot down over Sakhalin in 1983, compared unfavorably with the U.S. Navy's ability to identify an individual Egyptian airliner carrying the *Achille Lauro* terrorists in a crowded Mediterranean sky and to force it to land at Sigonella, Sicily, in 1985.

In the area of airborne early warning and control, the Soviets operated at a qualitative and quantitative disadvantage on the northern flank. The Il-76 Mainstay, a Russian version of the American E-3 Sentry—the AWACS—was central to Soviet airborne early warning and control. But the Mainstay, although a vast improvement over its predecessor, the ineffective Tu-126 Moss, was not qualitatively comparable to the AWACS, and was even inferior in many aspects to the U.S. Navy's carrier-borne E-2C Hawkeye.

Moreover, the Soviet Air Defense Force possessed only twenty Mainstays worldwide, of which four were deployed in the Kola at Umbozero S(outh). The United States and its European, Middle Eastern, and Asian allies possessed over seventy-five Sentries, and the U.S. Navy itself had over seventy Hawkeyes. The four American carriers steaming north towards the Barents Sea on the evening of 28 July carried nineteen Hawkeyes. And six American, two British, and two NATO AWACS operated from bases in Iceland, Norway, and the United Kingdom.

According to NATO planners, the seventy-plus SAM sites in the Kola were also not as formidable as they appeared on paper. At least half were obsolescent systems that the U.S. Navy had been jamming and fooling since the Vietnam War. And even many of the newer types of SAMs were ineffective against low flying targets. Moreover, the SAM sites operated independently, so no matter how modern and effective, they were limited in the number of enemy aircraft they could engage simultaneously and were difficult, if not impossible, to control centrally.

The most modern and advanced search radars in the Kola were tied to the Soviet Union's anti-ballistic missile (ABM) defensive system, and even here, the Soviets had only a single phased-array radar at Olenegorsk capable of providing Northwest Front with an overall picture of the confused air battle over the Kola.

The American Striking Fleet, by contrast, included seven Aegis platforms, six cruisers and one destroyer, whose phased-array radars provided a far more formidable air defense system than the more numerous Soviet SAMs deployed throughout the Kola.

A great deal of the responsibility for the Soviet air defense of the Kola, therefore, rested with the interceptors of the AADS. But losses had eroded Russian air strength. By the evening on 28 July the Soviets had lost 209 of the roughly 700 fixed-wing aircraft committed to the theater. Of the 200 fighters controlled by the AADS, LMD, and SNA, 87 had been lost. The four American carriers, on the other hand, still had about 140 F-14s and F/A-18s available, and the Royal Navy's *Invincible* and *Illustrious* carried fourteen Harriers. Additional NATO fighter support could also be called forth from northern Norwegian bases.

Soviet capability to strike the American battle fleet had also declined. Of the aircraft that posed any kind of offensive threat to the American carriers, a fifth of the 125 Backfires and Blackjacks had been lost, as well as about fifty of the 150 Badgers that began the campaign on, or subsequently reinforced, the Kola.

Moreover, of the score of airfields in the peninsula, only two—Olenegorsk and Schagui with their

Soviet Su-24 Fencer. Designed for use as a ground attack aircraft, Fencers were ineffective in an air-to-air role during the strike against the Kola.

4,600 meter runways—were Forward Operating Location (FOL) bases for Backfire and Blackjack strategic-capable bombers. Thus the major Soviet offensive threat to the American carriers was concentrated at just two airfields.

The American strike plan was fairly elaborate. On the evening of the 28th, the *Coral Sea* and

Theodore Roosevelt task forces would move south, as if they had been relieved. The ships would then steam in a clockwise semicircle to the north and head for the Barents Sea. Simultaneously, Kraus's CARSTRIKGRU TWO would steam north in the company of the Royal Navy's Third Squadron, with its two carriers, a reinforced STANAVFORLANT surface action group (designated SAG Alpha), and a Battleship Battle Group (BBBG) built around the Iowa (designated SAG Bravo). Attacks from the carriers were planned to begin at 1030 on the morning of 29 July. Fighters and ESM aircraft would fly high profiles, while attack planes flew low, using the mountains of northern Finnmark to hide from Soviet ground-based radar in the Kola.

Several ancillary operations were designed to supplement the attack by CARSTRIKGRUs ONE and TWO. RAF Phantoms and Buccaneers flying from north Norwegian bases would precede the carrier strikes, drawing Soviet fighters toward the south, spreading Soviet defenses. Meanwhile, American surface and subsurface platforms would fire sea-launched cruise missiles (SLCMs) against the FOL runways at Olenegorsk and Schagui.

Moreover, Vice Admiral Sigal intended to commence his assault with what he called his "trump cards." On board the *Theodore Roosevelt* when she left Norfolk were two aircraft under wraps in a corner of the hangar deck under twenty-four-hour Marine guard—a pair of U.S. Air Force F-117A Stealth fighters. Sigal had rejected plans to use the planes during the attack on the 23rd.

"They were my ace in the hole," Sigal later wrote, "and I kept waiting for the right moment to use them. The attack on the Kola was about as big a move as we were going to make."

The strike plan called for both "Wobbly Goblins" to be launched early on the 29th. Each would take out one of the two Mainstays that the Soviets kept airborne at any one time.

Sigal broached his plan for the Stealth fighters with U.S. Air Force Brigadier General Miller at their Bardufoss meeting on 26 July. Miller not only supported the idea, but also suggested that

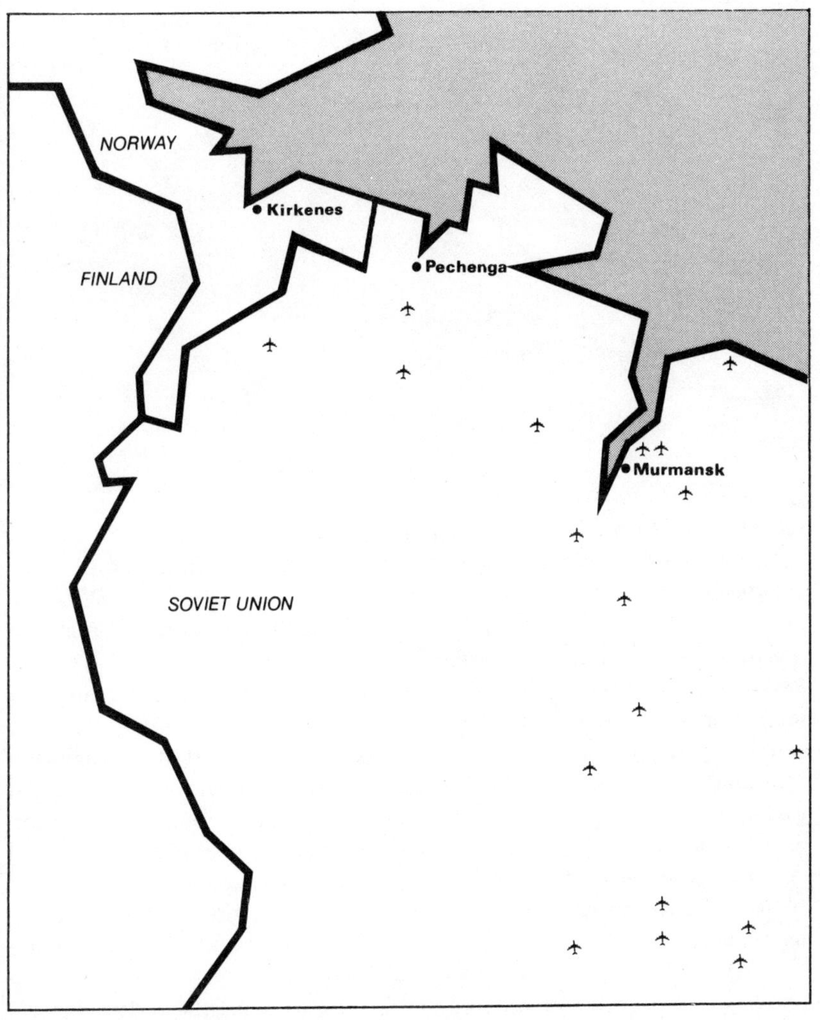

a second pair of F-117s join the attack and attempt to destroy the third and fourth Mainstays on the ground at Umbozero S. A C-5A Galaxy transporting two F-117s was scheduled to reach Evenes early on the 27th, where a forward operating base for the Stealth fighters would be established. Miller assured Sigal that these planes would be operational

Soviet air bases in the Kola. The heavily defended Kola proved vulnerable to an attack that exploited weaknesses of the Soviet command and control system.

USAF F-117A Stealth fighter. A pair of specially modified F-117As sailed aboard the Theodore Roosevelt when the war began. Whether or not they could be catapulted successfully, despite modifications to the front wheel assembly, was considered problematic. "Necessity," one Stealth pilot remarked, "remains the mother of invention."

no later than the evening of the 28th.

Sigal and Miller agreed to an outline plan for an expanded attack. The *Theodore Roosevelt* would launch a single F-117A against the northern Mainstay, and Evenes would send a F-117A to attack the southern Mainstay. The remaining two Stealth fighters, one from the *Theodore Roosevelt* and the other from Evenes, would attack Umbozero S. Both planes would carry French-made Durandal runway-penetration retarded bombs that would prevent the Soviets from getting additional Mainstays airborne.

The Goblin flying from the carrier would also carry Mk 35 IN Cluster bombs, for use if the Mainstays were, by chance, exposed on the runway at the time of the attack. The Evenes Stealth would carry CBU-72 Fuel Air Explosive (FAE) Overpressure bombs. Known as "Aerosol Bombs," the FAE warhead contained three heavier-than-air gases that were released into the air when the bomb struck the surface. They were then ignited by a delayed-action explosive, forming a massive fireball that would destroy most unhardened targets in the open. The FAE was devastating against enclosed structures, such as aircraft shelters. "It was the closest thing I ever saw to an A-bomb," one Air Force pilot commented.

Filling both ordnance bays of the F-117As scheduled to attack Umbozero S. with bombs meant that the Stealth fighters, which mounted no cannon or machine guns, could not carry any AMRAAMs or Sidewinders for self-defense. But that did not deter Captain Dale "Chip" Sharrick, who flew an Evenes-based F-117 against the Soviet airfield.

Sure it was dangerous, but it was the nature of the game, the nature of the program. They weigh the potential loss against the potential gain, and they tell you to take out the missiles and hang some extra bombs. And let's be honest. The Stealth fighter really wasn't a "fighter," it was a strike plane. If you ended up in a dogfight, you had made a mistake. Your primary defense was your ability to avoid enemy radars, and thus to avoid those things that could kill you. Our ideal mission was to get to and from the target without being detected, without being shot at, and without having to shoot at anyone. But . . . you still feel a hell of a lot safer up there when you have a few Sidewinders loaded in Bay One.

Late on 28 July, CARSTRIKGRU ONE steamed southwest in a move timed to take advantage of the absence of Soviet satellite coverage. The CVBG then altered course to the north while CARSTRIKGRU TWO, the British, STANAVFORLANT, and SAG Bravo steamed north.

Vice Admiral Weir moved one British and eight American subs into the Barents Sea earlier on the 28th to lead the offensive. This submarine force was dominated by American subs because many of the Royal Navy's subs after bearing the brunt of the defensive battle of 23 July, had returned to bases in Scotland for resupply and repair. The American boats, which began the war patrolling along the G-I-UK Gap, had initially assisted air and surface forces in their successful effort to "roll back" Soviet submarines toward their Kola bases. Now by the evening of 27 July, these U.S. Navy SSNs were entering the Barents Sea from the west and south.

However, Sigal's expectation that he could move his force north without being detected, as he had on the 23rd, was too sanguine. Anticipating such a possible move by NATO naval forces, the Soviets had adjusted the tracks of their satellites. Additionally, the weather failed to cooperate. Cloud cover was only about 60 percent.

Northwest Front was immediately aware of the Striking Fleet's movement. In response, Admiral Khomiakov hastily formed a Surface Strike Group in Pechenga Fiord. Its ships included the badly damaged battle cruiser *Frunze*, four cruisers (three of them damaged), six destroyers (one of them damaged), and a frigate. Meanwhile, three SSNs were vectored into patrol sectors along a line south of the North Cape.

The American sprint north also prompted renewed Soviet air attacks. In the early morning hours of the 29th, twenty-seven SNA Badgers, four of them ESM aircraft, escorted by forty-one AADS Foxbats and Foxhounds, concentrated over the Kola for a strike against the American carriers.

CARSTRIKFOR Tomcats intercepted the Soviet attackers over northern Norway. A Hawkeye pilot from the John F. Kennedy's VAW-126 Seahawks, later wrote:

The Russians shouldn't have stood a chance in hell. We picked them up as they were retracting their landing gear. We could have gotten every Turkey (Navy slang for the F-14 Tomcat) on all four carriers into an intercept, but they were holding a lot of them back for our own raid. With the six Ticos (Ticonderoga-class Aegis cruisers) with the fleet I don't think they were even worried about a few Badgers leaking through.

Eleven of the Soviet fighters and seventeen of the Badgers were downed. Three Tomcats were lost.

But two Badgers did penetrate the defenses. While Harriers from the *Illustrious* ended up downing both, the Tu-16Gs had enough time to launch a pair each of AS-5 Kelts. Three of the missiles were destroyed, but the fourth "flew through the kitchen sink" and struck the *Saratoga* forward, starboard side, at 0045. The hit knocked catapults out of action as damage control teams extinguished the fire. By 0215, the fire was out and the port bow catapult was operational. The starboard bow catapult, however, was destroyed beyond repair.

Meanwhile, as the crew of the *Saratoga* struggled to limit the damage to the ship, two Soviet SSNs that had eluded the NATO submarines screening the Striking Fleet attacked. Two torpedoes struck

Soviet Akula-class SSN. Soviet submarines, although only marginally inferior to British and American SSNs, nevertheless fared poorly in sub-surface three-dimensional engagements that had more in common with air-to-air combat than with traditional naval actions.

Soviet Oscar-class SSN. Oscars carry both cruise missiles and torpedoes. Submerged speed is 33 knots.

the Spruance-class destroyer *John Rodgers*. The ship, despite the valiant efforts of her crew, sank at 0430. A second spread of torpedoes narrowly missed the *Coral Sea*.

For the submarines of the Northern Fleet, however, the sinking of the *John Rodgers* was "the last hurrah." In fact, both Soviet SSNs, a Victor and an Oscar, were sunk by the Striking Fleet's ASW forces, supported by RAF Nimrods flying from Lossiemouth in Scotland and Norwegian P-3s from Andoya. Later in the day, NATO SSNs sank three additional Soviet submarines.

The campaign was at a turning point.

Blasting Kola

Goblins Attack Sanctuaries

Once it became clear that the Soviet air and submarine attacks had been successfully beaten off, and that the damaged *Saratoga* was still operational, Vice Admiral Sigal gave the order to commence GOLDEN TALON. Word was immediately passed to the Ready Room of the *Theodore Roosevelt's* VA-35 Black Panthers where U.S. Air Force Major Randolph "Roller" Ball and Captain Steven "Monk" Jackson were completing their briefing.

Major Ball had planned the strikes to avoid having both F-117s flying through the same defenses for fear that the detection of one of the planes would alert the Soviets and lead them to detect the other. Jackson's target was the northern Mainstay. He had to fly a longer, but somewhat safer route, and would time his approach so that he attacked the Mainstay between 0945 and 1000. His first leg was to the northeast, the second to the east. Jackson would then turn south, passing east of Murmansk, and hopefully intercept the Mainstay from the northeast. Ball, whose target was the airbase at Umbozero S., would fly a more

American attack submarine USS Groton (SSN-694). Groton and sister subs launched Tomahawk cruise missiles against base at Schagui in the Kola.

direct and heavily defended path over mountainous northern Norway, Finnish Lapland, and the Kola.

Ball planned to launch minutes after Jackson and would time his approach so that he would reach Umbozero S. between 1000 and 1015.

"We hoped," Captain Jackson later recalled, "that the delay would give the Russians time to react

and get their other Mainstays out on the runway, but not enough time to get them airborne, although we were prepared for that, too."

The two F-117s flying from Evenes planned their routes to conform to the attack planned by Ball. Major John "Darth" Vajda's F-117 was to fly a circuitous route over northern Sweden and

Finnish Lapland before crossing into the Kola and approaching the southern Mainstay from the southeast.

"At my briefing," Vajda wrote, "I raised the question of Swedish neutrality. Don't worry about it, I was told, they owe us one."

The second Evenes Stealth, piloted by Captain "Chip" Sharrick, flew a more direct route for Umbozero S.

If all went well, by the time the fighters and ESM aircraft of the CVBG passed over the northern Norwegian mountains at 0530, the two airborne Mainstays would be burning wrecks on the tundra, while damaged runways at Umbozero S. (there were two) would prevent the Soviets from getting replacements airborne for hours, if not for days.

"Monk" Jackson, who would launch first from the *Theodore Roosevelt*, hit the head one last time and caught the escalator to the flight deck. There he saw his F-117 being towed off the aft port deck elevator. He checked out his Goblin, climbed into the cockpit, started the General Electric F404 engines, and taxied to the starboard waist catapult.

I did all that aircraft carrier stuff. You know, the JBD (Jet Blast Deflector) came up, they hooked me up to the cat, and checked the weight. OK. The yellow shirt gave me the brakes off, full power signal. I flapped the controls and the green shirts checked the plane. I got the thumbs up and saluted. They did all that fancy hand signaling, and pow.

The cat shot was quite an experience. It was like getting hit in the rear of your car by a series of busses that just keep pushing you along. Three hundred feet in two seconds, quite a trip! I had done it twice before in an A-7, which I had flown for the Air Force before coming to the Stealth program, but this was my first cat shot in the F-117. I held the stick back as I launched, but held it too long. The next thing I knew I heard the Air Boss screaming "angle of attack, angle of attack, angle of attack" and I realized that I was airborne and going up too steep. I got the stick centered just in time before I stalled. That had been my one big fear—getting off the damned deck! And I almost blew it.

The time was 0748. Jackson's approach over the Barents Sea was uneventful. Data supplied from an AWACS allowed him to avoid passing within visual range of any of the Soviet warships that had sortied from Pechenga the previous day:

When I turned south, east of Murmansk, I had time to spare so I maximized my "stealthiness." I cut power way back, extended the flaps, and flew at about 200 feet. The ground was flat, so I didn't have to worry about flying into any mountains. A few minutes later I got a data burst from the AWACS controlling me. They had the Mainstay, bearing 190, about 150 kilometers from me. She wasn't alone. There were four fighters escorting her.

Not many people realize how dependent the Stealth is on AWACS. All of your systems are passive so you can't see very far. I planned my approach based on information the AWACS supplied. It told me where the Mainstay was long before I could locate it myself. It gave me positions on the fighters. You relied on your FLIR (forward looking infrared) camera for targeting, and that had a max range of forty to sixty miles depending on conditions.

I worked my way through the escorts, staying low and slow, and adjusting course as much as possible to stay outside their radar search cones. One Flanker cut across right in front of me at only fifteen kilometers.

At about thirty kilometers I located the Mainstay with my camera and at twenty-eight kilometers had her locked up. I was within firing range with the AMRAAM. But the Mainstay flew that racetrack pattern, kind of an oblong, and it was flying on a northeast-southwest axis. When it was flying northeast, we had a good closure, about 600 knots. I was doing about 250 and the Mainstay about 350. But when it turned away, the range extended. I knew it was about to turn again, so I held my lock and closed the range. I knew that if I had any chance to complete the mission and get out alive, I had to get it with the first missile. If I missed or just damaged it, and had to launch a second, I would probably end up dead.

Finally, the Mainstay came back toward me again. The range closed fast and at about twelve kilometers I pulled up to 500 feet, to give the AMRAAM some space to drop, opened the bay door, and fired. You carried everything internally on the Stealth. I launched a decoy, (a drone that continued on your course, speed, and altitude and had an enhanced electronic signature), closed the bay doors, and dove back down to about 200 feet. It took about ten seconds for the missile to reach the target. They were the longest ten seconds of my life. I just kept switching my eyes between the monitor and the ground praying, literally, that the missile didn't miss. Then I got a warning tone. The Mainstay had detected me. It startled me. We knew that the Russians had armed their Mainstays with AA-10s. We had lost a plane over Germany to one. And I suddenly had visions of trying to elude an Alamo at 200 feet. But then my missile ripped the port wing off the Mainstay. I began a shallow turn to port, keeping my radar profile as low as possible, and headed north.

After downing a Flanker during his escape, Jackson landed several hours later at Evenes, where he was joined by Major Vajda and Captain Sharrick. "Darth" Vajda had downed the southern Mainstay two minutes after Jackson downed his. Sharrick, however, had reached Umbozero S.

USS Valley Forge (CG-50) launches Tomahawk cruise missile against base at Olenegorsk. Tomahawks were the bane of Soviet air defense commanders in the Kola.

only to find the main 3,850-meter runway already cratered and a wrecked Mainstay on the 3,000 meter secondary runway.

I decided to drop my Durandals in the center of the runway and was completing the approach when I took a quick glance at the FLIR and noticed some movement near a large shelter off to the right of the northern end of the runway. Since the runway was already damaged I switched to the FAE, which was laser guided, and adjusted my course to starboard. I painted the hanger by its open front and at about a half mile opened the bay doors and dropped the pair of FAEs. I throttled up and pulled back on the stick. The Aerosol bombs had a large blast radius, but you couldn't turn away because you had to keep the target painted with the laser which was on the underside of the aircraft. The shock of their explosion shook the hell out of the plane, but everything held together. I jettisoned the Durandals and turned west, for home. I knew that I had destroyed whatever was in that shelter, but it

American sub-launched Tomahawk cruise missile rises from the depths. Tomahawks blasted major Kola bases with heavy conventional warheads.

wasn't until I landed at Evenes that I learned that I had actually gotten the fourth Mainstay.

According to unofficial Soviet accounts, about five minutes before Sharrick approached the airbase, Major Ball reached Umbozero S. and cratered the runway with a pair of Durandals. Seeing a Mainstay taxiing from a shelter along the secondary runway, he returned and destroyed the plane with Cluster bombs. His decision apparently cost him his freedom, if not his life. The Soviet Union has never acknowledged shooting down his plane and the U.S. government has been unable to verify reports that Ball was captured and the wreckage of his plane collected and shipped to Moscow. Major Ball is still listed as missing in action. For his valiant efforts, he was awarded the Medal of Honor.

With the Mainstays out of action, Soviet air defense of the Kola was disrupted, and the situation at AADS HQ at Archangelsk became confused. Nevertheless, the Soviets could sense that a major air attack was imminent. Ground radar detected American carrier aircraft as they crested the northern Norwegian mountains and strike aircraft from northern Norwegian bases over Finnish Lapland. Reports of visual sightings of cruise missiles came in from units in northern Norway, but the SLCMs had yet to show up on radar.

At that very moment, however, twenty-eight Tomahawk cruise missiles with conventional warheads were issuing from the mountain valleys of Finnmark. A dozen of the terrain-hugging missiles were on their way to the FOL airbase at Schagui, launched by the *Los Angeles*-class SSNs *Newport News*, *Salt Lake City*, and *Groton*; and another sixteen Tomahawks fired from the cruisers *Valley Forge*, *San Jacinto*, *Normandy*, and *Chancellorsville*, were on course for Olenegorsk.

But AADS had few resources with which to meet the immediate NATO air threat. Frontal Aviation assets, only a few of which were fighters, were committed to a support role for the Army. And of AADS's remaining eighty-five fighters, only sixty were operational and available for intercepts. Of those, the forty or so Kola-based Foxbats, Fencers, and Floggers were mediocre dogfighters and had little or no look-down/shoot-down capability to intercept and destroy the American SLCMs. Only the four-dozen Flankers, Foxhounds, and Fulcrums, of which at least a third were grounded, were qualitatively comparable to the American-built "Teen" fighters—the F-14s, F/A-18s, and F-16s—leading the NATO attack, and had a look-down/shoot-down capability.

Opposite: Soviet MiG-29 Fulcrum fighters. MiG-29 proved the most successful Soviet fighter of the war. Fitted with excellent avionics and missiles, plus an effective FLIR system, the Fulcrum fought well in the hands of skilled pilots, despite its lack of advanced "fly by wire" control systems.

Technologically blinded and psychologically stunned by the loss of all four Mainstays, AADS ground controllers never managed to get a grip on the air battle that raged over the Kola on the morning of 29 July.

Colonel Vorontsev, who visited the VPVO headquarters at Archangelsk, reported that the AADS headquarters was "in chaotic condition and unable to supply any coherent overall picture of the air situation."

Poor direction insured that the sixty or so fighters the Soviets managed to get airborne during the 29th would be unable to turn back the NATO attacks launched from the Striking Fleet's carriers and northern Norwegian airbases.

"Spud" Marsh later recalled:

Look, in virtually every category the Russians were at a disadvantage, at least a minor one. They had a poor or non-existent AWACS picture (I think they managed to get a few old Mosses up later in the day). They were outnumbered. Their aircraft, on the whole, were inferior. Their avionics

MiG-25 Foxbat was backbone of Soviet air defense fleet. Early research version set time-to-height records in the mid-1970s.

were inferior. Their air-to-air missiles were inferior. The ECM were inferior, and the training and skills of their pilots were inferior. Now, you take all of these minor inferiorities, you add them up and what do they spell? I'll tell you: s-l-a-u-g-h-t-e-r! We lost some planes, but the bottom line was that we reached the targets and hit them.

Eight Tomahawks struck Schagui; thirteen struck Olenegorsk. Runways were cratered and control towers were demolished. Scattered bomblets and delayed-action warheads made quick repairs impossible. While hardened shelters protected most of the Russian bombers, many were damaged or destroyed on the ground. Those that could still fly were unable to take off from cratered runways and remained vulnerable to follow-up strikes.

Some critics charged that the Navy's use of SLCMs against bases located in the Soviet Union was provocative, arguing that the Soviets, had they assumed that the Tomahawks were nuclear-armed, might have responded to perceived atomic attacks with an actual atomic retaliatory

strike of their own.

But Vice Admiral Sigal considered such reasoning faulty:

You have to look at these things in context. First, the flight profiles of atomic and conventional armed SLCMs differ. You can tell the difference when they're airborne, although I admit that it was possible for the Soviets, who were under attack, to miss such a fine point as profiles. Second, sure, we had SLCMs going in, but at the same time we had scores of strike planes flying low over the same terrain. SLCMs alone, yea, I guess you might think they could be nuclear; but SLCMs as part of a much larger strike? Hell, we would've been nuking our own planes right along with the Russians. Third, what's the difference between attacking an enemy with a Tomahawk or an Intruder? How were the Russians to know what kind of bomb we had strapped under an Intruder? If you follow the line of reasoning of some of the critics, you wouldn't be able to attack anyone anywhere with a missile or a plane.

As the air battle developed to NATO's advantage,

small groups of American A-6s and F/A-18s, supported by ESM aircraft, began their attacks on SAM sites, radar installations, command centers, and runways. By noon, forty-two Soviet fighters and fifty bombers had been downed or destroyed on the ground.

As the raids continued in the afternoon, Soviet resistance became increasingly uncoordinated, confused, and weak. The American offensive rolled across the Kola. By the end of the day, another eighty aircraft had been destroyed as well as numerous SAM installations and other facilities. American losses totaled twenty-one aircraft.

The attacks continued on the 30th. Most surviving Soviet aircraft at operational airbases were withdrawn east of Archangelsk, beyond the range of the American planes. The few remaining fighters, including Frontal Aviation assets, put up a gallant, but pointless fight. Only a half-dozen fighters, about fifty Badgers, Backfires, and Blackjacks, and about 110 reconnaissance, ASW, EW, and transport aircraft survived the second day of intensive attacks, either by escaping to other fields or by riding out the strikes in hardened shelters. About 350 Soviet planes were lost, including over 100 fighters. Moreover, most of the SNA's strike planes were destroyed on the ground. NATO losses totaled thirty-one U.S. Navy aircraft, five RAF, and a single Norwegian Falcon.

To the U.S. Navy, the Kola victory represented a vindication of its Maritime Strategy, its concept of operations, and its training. In his report to President Rush, CNO Dunn attributed the Navy's success in GOLDEN TALON to the establishment of Strike—the U.S. Naval Strike Warfare Center at Fallon, Nevada.

Commander Mick Simmonds, one of the GOLDEN TALON planners commented:

Had we tried to mount such an attack in the early or even the mid-1980s, I think we would have gotten the shit kicked out of us. But the planners, and many of the aviators, too, had been to Strike. You learned to put it all together at Fallon the easy way, in simulated training, and not the hard way, in the middle of an IADS (Integrated Air Defense System). It was sort of Top Gun for the strike community, except that we included the fighter jocks as well.

I'll give you a few examples of what I mean. We knew that we would be within range to attack early in the morning of 31 July, and Admiral Sigal wanted to attack ASAP. Now Sigal was a great fleet commander, but he had not been to Strike and some of his ideas were . . . a little out of date. He wanted to launch an early morning attack that would have had us flying right into the sun. It may seem like a minor point, but if you're flying an Intruder a couple of hundred feet off the ground, and you have the sun right in your eyes for an hour or two, it's a factor. When we explained this to the Admiral, he understood.

Then there was the question of altering plans. We had everything worked out when we received a message from the RAF at Bardufoss requesting a last minute alteration of some routes. One of the lessons we had learned in Lebanon in 1983 was that that was frequently a bad idea. We had stressed at Strike the basic concept that plans were not changed at the last minute. Sigal backed us up and we told the Brits to change their plans, because we weren't going to alter ours.

People don't realize all the factors that go into planning a strike. The days of the old Alpha strike—launch all the planes and send them over the target—are long gone. To pull off a successful strike today involves sophisticated, complicated, computer-assisted planning. You have to establish

U.S. Navy E-2C Hawkeye. The Hawkeyes were the key to effective battle group defense and air-space management during strikes against Soviet naval assets and bases in the Kola.

your mission, what it is you wish to accomplish. You have to select and identify your targets and determine what you know about them and what you don't know. What types of ordnance do you need to destroy them? Some of the intelligence you need you can get yourself, from TARPS, Tomcats specially outfitted for reconnaissance. But other information must come from other sources. You have to identify them and get the information promptly. You have to review your own assets—aircraft, Tomahawk-armed ships and submarines, personnel. You review the enemy's ORBAT (order of battle) as well.

Then you have weaponeering. What types of ordnance are available? How long does it take

to load the ordnance? What platforms are available to carry the ordnance? You have a launch cycle and you can only handle so many planes on the deck at one time. You can't have every plane carrying ordnance that takes forever to load. You have threat suppression. Some SAMs can be avoided, some need to be neutralized, some need to be destroyed. Routes and timing have to be established. You have to determine TOT (time over target). When do you want a given platform over the target? When you fly a lot of low altitude profiles, you don't want to have six planes hitting the target simultaneously. They would end up catching each other in their blast radii.

Now TAMPS (Tactical Air Mission Planning

System) helps a lot. We had programs loaded that covered the Kola targets and TAMPS can lay out the mission routes for you, but, with a complex mission like GOLDEN TALON, you have quite a bit of work to do.

Execution of the strike plan went fairly smoothly. If Soviet fighters appeared, the Hummers (E-2C Hawkeyes) would vector Tomcats or Hornets, with some Prowlers, to the area. After they dispatched the Russian fighters, other Prowlers and Intruders would jam the Russian SAMs sites, force them to shut down, or take them out with HARM. Then the Intruders and Hornets would come in at low level and destroy the target: Durandals on the runways, Paveways and FAEs on the hangers and towers, Cluster bombs on parked planes, Mavericks on the radars. We used a lot of the laser-guided stuff, PGMs. We bombed fuel depots, bridges, port facilities. You name it, we put ordnance on it. It was a hell of a forty-eight hours. That everything worked out as well as it did is a tribute to the work those guys at Strike do.

Throughout the 29th, the Striking Fleet continued its movement north, slowed by the constant need to turn into the prevailing southwest wind to launch and recover planes, and by concerns about the approach of the *Frunze* KUG rounding the North Cape. During the evening of 29 July, carrier aircraft were diverted from their planned Kola strikes to attack the Soviet surface group as it closed the range with STANAVFORLANT. At 1933 hours, A-6s from the *Saratoga* sank the damaged *Frunze.*

At 2305, SAG Alpha launched a SSM attack on the Soviets and began the "Battle off the North Cape." In the confused engagement between STANAVFORLANT and KUG 1, the Soviets lost the destroyer *Sderzhannyy* but managed to sink the West German destroyer *Molders.* The following morning the action intensified as the frigates *Active* (British) and *Bergen* (Norwegian) were sunk.

At first, the Soviets appeared to be taking control of the battle, despite the incessant NATO air attacks. But by 0245, Tomahawks and Harpoons from SAG Bravo, and the *Iowa* BBBG, reinforced by several "shooters" detached from the American CVBGs, ended the Northern Fleet's final bid for victory at sea. When the cruiser *Kursk* and the destroyers *Stroynyy* and *Vasil'yevskiy* were sunk, it became clear that the Soviet counterattack had failed. The remnants of KUG 1 "retired at high speed."

By 30 July, NATO aircraft, even long-range patrol planes, roamed freely over the Barents Sea. Air attacks finished off KUG 1's remaining two cruisers, three destroyers, and a frigate, for the loss of two planes. Other attacks cost the Soviets two more submarines and twenty-one surface ships, many of them caught at anchor in bases along the Kola coast.

Soviet naval power on the Northern Flank had been broken. Surviving SSNs fled under the ice for their own safety and to insure the security of Soviet "Boomers" which were now vulnerable to NATO submarine attacks for the first time since the *Warspite* and *Jack* had penetrated the Barents bastion on 21 July. Surface ships made their way east along the Arctic coast, led by Soviet icebreakers.

But Vice Admiral Sigal, after rounding the North Cape, retired once again to the south.

That was another of those decisions for which I've been criticized. But I had lost thirty-one planes. That may not sound like many, compared to what the Russians lost, but it was something like 12 percent of what I had had on the morning of the 29th. You're talking about a loss rate of 6 percent a day. A week of that and half your planes are gone. I could have kept up the pressure on the Kola airfields, but we were looking at diminishing returns. In my view, going against the Kola had never been an end in itself, it was a means to an end—gaining command of the sea in the North Atlantic and gaining command of the air, not over the Kola, but over northern Norway.

You couldn't find a Soviet plane over northern Norway by the afternoon of the 30th. And I knew that with their fighter arm destroyed, and with their bombers smashed on the ground or stranded at airbases with cratered runways, by the time they recovered from our attacks, the campaign would be over in Norway, one way or the other. We had drawn the remnants of the surface and submarine forces into battle and eliminated them. So, in my view, it was time to steam south, replenish our supplies, and use our air and surface bombardment assets to support the land battle. We had defeated their Navy; we had defeated their Air Forces; now we had to defeat their Army.

As Sigal's ships headed south, the Soviet Sixth Army prepared to launch a full scale assault on NATO positions in Fortress Norway.

End Game in Finnmark

Marines at the Kill

At 2000 on 30 July Generals Bagdasarian, Liashchenko, and Pokrovsky met at Sixth Army headquarters at Kautokeino. But the worsening situation in the air over the Kola made it impossible for Northwest Front commander General Kovalesky, who had ordered the meeting, to fly from Murmansk to the front.

The mood of the conference was somber. As Major General Bagdasarian recalled:

Things were obviously not going well. The 54th Corps attack had been repulsed. Tromso, which we had intended to establish as a forward base to support the operations of the Front airmobile brigade, had been retaken. The enemy's air force controlled the skies and reports from Murmansk indicated that the air battle up north was going abysmally. Pokrovsky asked for my recommendation for a future course of action and I suggested that we withdraw. Matvei Ivanovich (Liashchenko) agreed. But the commanding general called us "defeatists."

I stressed that an attacking force concentrated along a single road could not possibly operate successfully in the face of uncontested enemy air control. I remember well that the Army commander had just finished explaining to me how I was exaggerating the extent of the air problem when several explosions rocked the conference room. We were meeting in a camouflaged prefabricated structure just outside Kautokeino. We ran for the slit trenches, but the raid was already over. We walked toward the village and learned that enemy aircraft (American Marine Corps A-6s) had bombed the Tourist Hotel and the Kautokeino Youth Hostel, which Sixth Army had taken over to house the staff. Many senior officers were killed. We stood there stunned as some Lapps were pressed into a rescue team. I turned to Pokrovsky and said, "Is this an exaggeration?"

Despite this firsthand evidence of the deteriorating air picture and the desire of his corps commanders to withdraw, Pokrovsky remained determined to advance. He argued that the release of 111 Motorized Rifle Division (MRD) from Front reserve on 29 July had dramatically altered the correlation of forces. Two regiments were heading south along the E-6 through Finnmark. Two more were taking up positions near Tornio where they had relieved the brigades of the 54th Corps that had been covering the left flank of the Soviet advance.

It was imperative that Bagdasarian and Liashchenko continue their attacks. Even if they failed to break through, their assault would so exhaust the defenders that the arrival of fresh troops from the second echelon would ultimately overwhelm NATO forces.

"It is just a question of time," Pokrovsky said, "until the enemy collapses."

But Bagdasarian and Liashchenko considered Pokrovsky's reasoning "overoptimistic." The 111th MRD was a category B division with old equipment, manned by reservists, still saddled with the old

The amphibious ship Saipan (LHA-2) in the Norwegian Sea late on 31 July.

divisional structure. More importantly, its regiments, and the two brigades of the 54th Corps coming from Tornio, were still hundreds of miles from the front. To Bagdasarian, rapid movement of large motorized formations several hundred miles along a single road without air cover was impossible.

The 45th Corps commander also believed that Pokrovsky's determination to attack was rooted less in his operational assessment than in his political judgment. Kovalesky, whose failures thus far had earned him little praise from Moscow, was desperate to achieve a victory that could now only come from his ground forces, and that pressure was passed down the chain of command to Sixth Army.

Pokrovsky ordered his subordinates to attack. Liashchenko's 54th Corps would have to resume the drive on Rosta. Bagdasarian's 45th Corps would push along the roads on either side of the Lyngen Fiord. Elements of three 45th Corps brigades would launch a concentrated assault against a battalion of the 13th Norwegian Brigade and the British Paras. And since no Frontal Aviation support was available, Sixth Army would rely on its attack helicopter assets to support the offensive and mobile SAMs and AAA to provide air defense.

However, the Front airmobile brigade, which had earlier unhinged COMNON's left flank, would only be able to provide limited assistance to the 45th Corps offensive since Wunderlin's costly counterstroke against Tromso had destroyed the forward base established to support the operations of the helicopter-borne force. Allied control of the air also made it impossible to fly additional supplies forward.

In the end, Pokrovsky was forced to pull two of the three remaining battalions back to Nordreisa, along the E-6 north of the Lyngen Fiord. A single battalion, all that could be sustained in combat with the supplies on hand, ended up supporting the 45th Corps's attack by establishing a blocking position along the E-6 midway between the Bals Fiord and the Malselv River.

Hours before the Sixth Army's attack began at 1000, NATO aircraft, in an effort to disrupt the coming offensive, began striking Soviet forces concentrated along the roads and in the valleys.

"We suffered significant losses," one Russian battalion commander wrote, "before the attack even began."

That the offensive got underway at all, the Soviets owed principally to their air defenses. And even though the mountainous Norwegian terrain reduced the effectiveness of the larger Soviet SAMs and radar-controlled AAA platforms, such as the ZSU-24 "Zeus," smaller, shoulder-launched, heat-seeking missiles, such as the SA-7B Grail, proved effective.

"It's quite a trick to evade a heat seeker in a valley," one RAF pilot wrote. "You have to rely on flares, trees, and prayer, because you have so little room to maneuver to the sides."

NATO ground attack pilots developed a healthy respect for Soviet air defenses, but a respect that lasted only as long as the supply of SAMs which, by the end of the day, were running short with no prospect of resupply.

Despite the heavy losses and disruption caused by the NATO air attacks, Sixth Army's offensive began on schedule. Liashchenko's troops advanced three kilometers before encountering a Brigade North battalion that had relieved the German Gebirgsjägers. The Norwegians, after repulsing Russian attacks throughout the day, held the ground the West Germans had won.

Bagdasarian's 45th Corps, on the other hand, by the sheer weight of its assault, pushed forward ten miles, wresting control of Nordkjosbotn from its Norwegian defenders shortly before midnight. But there the advance stalled under steady air attack. Every effort to get the troops moving again failed as Breivik and Heinzen fed reinforcements into the battle and NATO resistance stiffened.

Ship-to-shore movement of Marines of the II MEF, evening 31 July.

To prevent any Soviet forces that broke through the front from racing along the E-6, seizing the Malselv River bridge, and overrunning the airbase at Bardufoss, Major General Breivik deployed the Norwegian 15th Brigade's 1st battalion in reserve astride the road north of Andselv. The inability of the Soviets to conduct aerial reconnaissance left Sixth Army unaware of the Norwegians' presence.

The attempted Russian heliborne assault proved to be a fiasco. It was as poorly executed as it had been planned, and was bloodily repulsed. The remnants of the battalion landed in some open ground five miles east of the E-6, where they were immediately attacked by Norwegian and Italian troops that were moving toward the front.

Breivik and Heinzen responded promptly to the Soviet offensive, moving reserves to the threatened sector. Throughout 1 August, five Norwegian battalions, the entire ACE Mobile Force, and the NCFN launched concentric counterattacks against the Soviet penetration. And Norwegian, Dutch, British, and American ground attack aircraft pounded Russian positions with increasing intensity as Soviet air defense units exhausted their supplies of SAMs. By noon the Italian Susa Alpini battalion, well supported by the 40th battery of the Pinerolo Mountain Artillery Group, had eliminated the LMD airhead.

The Italians, who left most of their heavy equipment in the rear, found themselves astride a minor road that connected with the E-6 north of Nordkjosbotn. Major Dante Sufferdini led his men along the track and, meeting no resistance, soon reached the E-6. He ordered his men to entrench.

The movement of the Italian mountain troops took the Soviets by surprise. Suddenly, the retreat

USMC Harriers return after support mission. Marine Harriers proved their worth during the campaign. They provided quick reaction support by their ability to base forward close to the battle, despite Soviet destruction of airfields in North Norway.

of the Soviet 253rd Brigade was blocked. In response, Bagdasarian ordered an attack designed to reopen the road. To do the job, he sent a mixed tank/motor rifle force, which promptly assaulted the Italians. Captain Emidio Di Pasquo commanded one of the Susa's companies.

The Russian attack came suddenly. We knocked out several BMPs and forced their infantry to dismount. We pinned them down with automatic weapons. Our rockets destroyed four T-72s but the others—there must have been at least twenty tanks—overran our positions. But they, too, were now trapped in the pocket. We were being attacked from all sides and men were dropping everywhere. But they kept fighting in this inferno. We held on until some Jaguars arrived and bombed the Russians as they were preparing for another assault.

Late in the day, in extremely heavy fighting, the NCFN retook Nordkjosbotn and relieved the hard-pressed Italians. By then, the Susa Alpini had lost 350 of 600 men, including their commander. But the gallant defense along the E-6 led to the

USMC Harriers preparing for ground support mission.

destruction of the isolated Soviet Brigade and cost the 45th Corps over thirty tanks. Overall, in the fighting on 31 July and 1 August, both sides suffered between 3,000 and 4,000 casualties, but the Soviet drive south had been stopped.

As the Soviet 45th Corps struggled slowly forward on 31 July, Hank Wunderlin, from his perch on the *Mount Whitney*, initiated a series of operations meant "to deliver the coup de grace to the Russians in Norway." At Bodo a combined Norwegian, British, and American force overran the remnants of the 76 Guards Airborne Division and recaptured the airbase.

The capture of Bodo meant that the 4 MEB, 42 Commando, and eight Norwegian battalions (many of them weakened after days of heavy fighting) were finally free for operations farther north.

But Wunderlin had no intention of waiting for these forces to move north before launching his next operation. After being relieved by the Dutch Marines at Tromso, 45 Commando and 6 MEB demonstrated their amphibious and airmobile capability by moving to the head of the Alta Fiord. At 1900 on 31 July, elements of 6 MEB and the Royal Marines, transported by helicopter directly from Tromso, landed between Talvik and Elvebakken. And at 1945, the remaining units of 6 MEB commenced ship to shore movement.

The American and British Marines encountered garrison troops from the Murmansk Division responsible for rear area security, but resistance was generally disorganized and light. By the evening of 1 August, Alta was in Allied hands and the E-6 was cut deep in the 45th Corps' rear. Despite a fairly effective Soviet effort to destroy the runways at the Alta airbase, Marine AV-8B Harriers from the amphibious assault ship *Saipan* began operating immediately from the newly captured airfield to provide air support for the troops.

As soon as the airfield was secure, Wunderlin choppered ashore and went to the Altafjord Vertshus, a hotel his staff had chosen as a site to establish II MEF Forward headquarters. To everyone's surprise, the telephone lines between Alta and the Finnmark towns farther north were still working. Through this link, Wunderlin was provided excellent information about Soviet dispositions throughout the county, which only reinforced his determination to push forward rapidly. Once satisfied that the headquarters was operational, he drove to the airport and took off once more in a helicopter to conduct a personal reconnaissance of the situation in the "fiordhead."

He soon spotted trouble at the bridge where the E-6 crossed the Altaelv River. What ensued, many of the Sixth Marines will long remember.

One company commander recounted the incident:

It was like that scene in the movie Patton where George C. Scott gets out in the mud and gets the two columns moving. It had rained, and it was muddy, and there were vehicles that had landed farther north along the coast which were to move to Alta, while the main column was headed in the opposite direction.

There was this massive congestion at the bridge when Wunderlin flew over in his chopper. It hovered there for a minute and then began to land. He didn't even wait. He must have jumped out when it was still about five or six feet up. He ran over toward the bridge and started chewing people out unmercifully. Next thing we knew there was Abe (the men called him "Abe" because he looked a little like Lincoln) signaling us forward. We were moving again. All the men cheered and gave the thumbs up sign as they went by. They

The Saipan rides out a summer storm. Marine battalion landing teams can move from ship to shore in her helicopters and landing craft.

just loved that guy. We all knew that he took care of his people.

Wunderlin had served three tours in Vietnam, his first in 1965 as an enlisted man, and his second and third as an officer. In 1970 he won the Navy Cross for rescuing a wounded point-man when his squad was ambushed. Wunderlin was badly wounded in the attempt. It was this same kind of selfless concern for his men that he brought to the operations in northern Norway.

My role as MAGTAF commander was to shape the battlefield for the kid on the ground. They did the hard, dirty fighting, and my concept of operations was to control the battle in such a way, especially with air power and mobility, that my Marines saw as few T-72s or T-80s as possible, and never had to attack a strongpoint frontally.

Such considerations figured into his choice of Alta as the base for II MEF operations.

I had landed at Alta before, on paper back in 1989 up at Newport during an exercise. I had walked, driven, and flown over northern Norway often during my career. I called the country "the Chameleon" because of the dramatic seasonal changes and their impact on amphibious and airmobile operations.

I often joked that I picked Alta to land because it was probably the premier salmon fishing site in the world. And it's true that when I went ashore on 1 August I took my fishing gear (and several hunting rifles) with me. But I didn't expect to have any time to fish. I saw them as a source of encouragement: to finish the campaign as quickly as possible so I could get in some good fishing.

Operationally, Alta was an ideal spot. The approaches through the fiord were good. It had an airfield and open ground for the Harriers and helicopters. You could cut the E-6 there far enough behind any Soviet troops assaulting the Fortress area that they couldn't easily turn about and fall on you, yet far enough away from any Russian reserves in the Kola that you had time to establish yourself ashore before getting hit. From Alta, you made the peninsula between the Alta and Porsangen Fiords impossible to hold. And you also could move south by the road through Kautokeino that connected the E-6 and the E-78 and threaten the Russian troops operating out of the Finnish Wedge. The whole idea was to put the enemy on the horns of a dilemma with multiple threats. That, combined with the MAGTAF's mobility, maximized the impact of the landing.

Wunderlin had long been convinced that the MEF-sized MAGTAF would be the key to victory in any campaign on the Northern Flank.

You have to understand what the MEF/MAGTAF was. It was a combined arms force of over 50,000 men, capable of sustained combat for up to sixty days. The Marines' air and sea mobility and air-ground cooperation was more highly developed than in any army in the world. And Norway, with its long coast and few roads was perfect for MAGTAF operations.

The MAGTAF in Norway was also the link between the Striking Fleet with its significant air power, and NATO forces in northern Norway. We were the link between the NATO AWACS and the fleet. We were the link between the campaign ashore and the campaign at sea, not just figuratively, but in the area of communications. The effective operation of the MAGTAF generated a synergistic effect between the two campaigns that might otherwise have become divorced.

Surrender and Stability

Northern Flank Secured

The collapse of the Soviet Sixth Army's offensive in Troms and the landing of Wunderlin's Anglo-American amphibious force in Finnmark created consternation in Moscow. Northwest Front's defeat at sea had been followed by defeat in the air, and now apparent defeat on land. Stavka was aware of the friction among the various commanders at front, army and corps level, as well as the lack of full cooperation and coordination between the services.

A concerned Minister of Defense, Marshal Yuri Vladimirov, the chief architect of the war, decided to fly to Murmansk and Northwest Front headquarters to gauge the situation firsthand. Marshal Nikolai Rodzianko accompanied Vladimirov who, should Kovalesky appear to be out of control, was prepared to replace the Northwest Front commander.

Allied intelligence learned of Vladimirov's intent to fly north as well as his ETA at Murmansk airport—1335 on 2 August. The source of this information, how it was obtained, and even the individual country which acquired it, remains a

An-72 Coaler, transport aircraft for senior Soviet commanders. Its short takeoff and landing qualities were valuable in that role.

secret. Nevertheless, at 1937 hours on 1 August, USAF Brigadier General Miller received an order to send a single F-117A Stealth fighter over the Kola to intercept Vladimirov's An-72 Coaler as it flew toward Murmansk. The planned intercept was given the code name TREATED LUMBER.

Miller called together his three Stealth pilots and asked for a volunteer. When all three pilots stepped forward, as he had expected, Miller produced a deck of cards. Major "Darth" Vajda, the senior pilot, and oddly enough a former seminarian, drew the high card.

It was a weird sensation. I knew that knocking down such a high-ranking officer would surely be a blow to the Russians, not just to their chain

of command, but to their morale. And there was a sense of satisfaction in the idea of downing this guy who had played a very real role in starting the damned war. It was also nice to know that the bigshots got killed sometimes too, not just the men at the front. But then again, was it war or murder?

We were talking, and the Yamamoto mission from the Pacific war kept coming up. And I remembered seeing a documentary on the Japanese admiral's life. They had interviewed the American P-38 pilot who shot him down. And this guy had been troubled by what he had done for forty years.

How did I feel, personally? Let me put it this way. I had quit smoking about six months before the war started, as a birthday present to my wife. Well, when I came out of that briefing with Miller, the first thing I did was to bum a cigarette. I haven't stopped smoking since.

At 1200 "Darth" Vajda's F-117 took off from Evenes. His flight plan would bring him to a position about sixty miles south of Murmansk where he could intercept Vladimirov's Coaler before it began its final approach to land.

I flew through the Norwegian valleys at 200 feet. As I crossed into Finland, the terrain flattened out and I started getting indications of SAM radars, but I flew on undetected. There were plenty of Russian fighters airborne, but they were mostly MiG-21s and a few Floggers. They had no lookdown capability and posed little threat. My only concern was that I still had no data from the AWACS on the Coaler's position.

I reached the waypoint south of Murmansk on schedule and turned south. Suddenly I started picking up some good Soviet fighters—Fulcrums, Flankers, Foxhounds—and a Moss on my FLIR camera. My guess was that they were there to escort Vladimirov's plane. They were headed directly at me. I held my course staying low, at 200', but I began to worry that the Moss might pick me up.

Finally, a data burst from the Sentry indicated that two additional planes were flying due north behind this first wave of interceptors. Assuming that one of these aircraft was the Coaler, I flew on until the Moss's radar signal became dangerously strong. I didn't think that I had the speed to make a detour and come up from behind. I pulled up, opened the bay, and fired an AMRAAM at about ten kilometers—I blew his lips off.

I dove for the hard deck and prayed. The Russian fighters were obviously anxious but failed to detect me. They flew right over me. I started to climb again and picked up the Coaler, with a Foxbat on its wing, at about thirty-four kilometers. I flew on and at 15 kilometers I ripple-fired a pair of AMRAAMs. I got a kill on the MiG-25 but the second missile missed. I switched to Sidewinders, throttled up, and climbed steeply. The Coaler was almost past me when I got off the AIM-9 at two kilometers. I hosed him. I had climbed to almost 3,000 feet, so I launched a decoy and dove, turning to starboard. They never knew what hit them.

My return to Evenes went smooth, too smooth. I got careless. I was flying down this Norwegian valley when I got a warning light—a heat seeker. Some Russian troops must have moved into that valley. They fired a Grail at me. I punched out flares and turned as hard as I could without hitting the mountain. The explosion rocked the plane. I lost power momentarily, but I pulled up, throttled up, and leveled off. Some of my avionics were out, including the ILS, but I was close enough to get back home.

The deaths of Marshals Vladimirov and Rodzianko shook the command structure in the Northwestern TSMA, as well as the entire Soviet Union. At Northwest Front and Sixth Army, the failure of the Soviet offensive in northern Norway finally became obvious. The Soviets had no choice but to begin to withdraw back toward the Kola.

Lieutenant General Liashchenko reported that his 54th Corps, despite reinforcement by the two brigades from Tornio and the possession of a firm left flank along the Swedish border, was incapable of holding its positions. The lead units were battered, and the columns moving forward along the E-78 were under constant air attack, strikes that also interdicted the movement of supplies to the front. Only the inability of the battle-weary Norwegian units opposite Liashchenko's troops to advance allowed the Soviets to hold a line west of Heligskoggen until 6 August when the 54th Corps began an orderly retreat into Lapland.

The 45th Corps, however, was in total disarray, harassed by constant air attacks, and trapped between COMNON forces in the south and Wunderlin's Marines to the north. Worse still for the beleaguered corps, early in the morning of 2 August, the NATO Composite battalion reached the head of Lyngen Fiord and cut the 45th Corps in two. Bagdasarian had little choice but to make a hasty retreat.

Meanwhile, Pokrovsky's only reserve, the remaining two battalions of the LMD airmobile brigade, were moved back to Kautokeino to

The battleship Iowa provides fire support for Marine operations ashore.

protect Sixth Army headquarters and the rear of 54th Corps from a possible II MEF advance from Alta. At the same time, the 111th MRD raced to beat Wunderlin's Marines to Lakselv and the airfield at Banak, held by the battalion of the 45th Corps' 10th Brigade which had been blockading Hammerfest.

But the withdrawal of Soviet forces from Hammerfest had released two Norwegian battalions for further operations. Breivik immediately placed these troops under II MEF control. Losing no time, Wunderlin moved them to Alta where one battalion served as a base garrison force while the other moved south along the E-6 to block the retreat of 45th Corps from the Lyngen area. This freed 45 Commando and 6 MEB for a 2 August advance on Lakselv from the west while the battalion of 4 MEB withdrawn from Bodo landed north of the town near Hamnbukt.

The Allied attack, supported by the 16-inch guns of the battleship *Iowa*, attack helicopters, Hornets and Intruders from the carriers, and U.S. Marine fixed-wing aircraft and helicopter gunships, overwhelmed the Soviet defense. Satisfied with the operations so far, Wunderlin quickly consolidated his position and prepared for the expected counterattack by the 111th MRD.

Meanwhile, back at Bardufoss, Breivik, too, sought to accelerate the tempo of operations. Soviet resistance was clearly weakening, and reports from the front indicated that Russian soldiers were beginning to surrender in appreciable numbers.

But the Norwegians were exhausted. And scores of Soviet vehicles abandoned along the E-6 posed major obstacles to rapid movement. The NATO Composite battalion managed to advance only twelve miles in forty-eight hours, recapturing Lyngseidet late on 3 August. The

West German Gebirgsjägers retook Skibotn about the same time.

That evening, Breivik and Heinzen met at Nordkjosbotn. The West German general spoke frankly.

I told Hans that it was obvious that his troops had had it. They were, after all, reservists. They were well trained; they knew the terrain; they fought bravely and excellently on the defensive. But their battalions were smaller and less heavily armed than the NATO battalions. I suggested that his infantry should go over to the defensive and that we should rely on the ACE and the Composite Force, supported by Norwegian Leopards and artillery, for the counteroffensive.

Things were working out that way in any case. But by making it official, we could move the tired units out of the way and concentrate my brigade for a drive north along the E-6. Nevertheless, it was a difficult situation for him. His national command and his country's pride, as well as his own, was at stake. But he saw the virtue in my recommendation. He recognized that he would, for all intents and purposes, be turning over responsibility for the counteroffensive to me, but he agreed. Our staffs worked out the details.

On the 4th, the pace of the advance began to improve. Within two days, the remnants of the 45th Corps were pocketed at the head of the Kvaenangen Fiord near Kvaenangsbotn along the E-6.

On the morning of 6 August, three Soviet soldiers bearing a white flag approached the lines of the British parachute battalion. The Russians informed a British captain that their general, Bagdasarian, wished to discuss terms of surrender.

At 0345 the 45th Corps commander arrived at the forward headquarters of the ACE Mobile Force. In his memoirs, Generalmajor Heinzen described the occasion.

We met and shook hands and identified each other. We then retired to my command tent where we could discuss matters in private. Although I did not speak Russian, and he did not speak German, we were able to converse in English and needed no translators. Bagdasarian said that he was prepared to surrender.

I asked him, "Are you here to surrender your command?"

He repeated what he had said before, that he was prepared to surrender.

"But are you here actually to surrender, right here, now?" I continued.

He paused and then said that was why he had come and that the killing had to stop. I then apologized but informed him that I did not feel that I could accept his surrender, that COMNON, General Breivik, should receive it.

I said that I could provide a helicopter to take him to Bardufoss. But Bagdasarian was reluctant to do that. He felt that the surrender would go more smoothly if he was there to insure that his troops complied. I understood his concern and asked him to wait while I went to the communications tent and talked to General Breivik. He agreed that it might be best for him to fly to my headquarters. I think he was especially happy that I had refused to accept the Russian's surrender and had allowed him the honor.

Bagdasarian was a beaten man, unshaven and unwashed. I had some food brought for him and offered him my razor since I was sure that the Norwegians would want to photograph the surrender. He thanked me profusely.

While we waited for Breivik to arrive, about an hour and a half, we had a very frank discussion. He was bitter about the fate of his command and spoke disparagingly of his superiors. He then began to attack the entire Communist system in the Soviet Union. I asked him if he had always had such doubts. He said they had begun while he was serving in Afghanistan, "a butcher's war," he called it. Apparently, while he was in Kabul, his wife and children were killed in the Armenian earthquake of 1988. Then he had begun to question the system.

He began to speculate about the ultimate fate of the Soviet system should they lose the war. He asked me if I thought Communism would survive in Russia. I replied that I was not a Sovietologist and really could form no opinion, but that I hoped that it would. I believe he thought I had misspoken in English, and he repeated the question.

But I assured him that I understood, and that I hoped Communism would survive. He asked why, and I told him that I considered the West fortunate that Russia was ruled by such incompetents. I said that if capitalists had ruled Russia since 1917, his would have been the most powerful nation on earth.

He looked at me in disbelief and then began to laugh. "So let us drink," he said, "to the survival of the Communist way of life in my motherland." And we drank a toast—schnapps. When Breivik arrived, Bagdasarian surrendered. We took about 5,500 prisoners.

At 2100 on 3 August, Lieutenant General Wunderlin had requested that Vice Admiral Sigal fly to Alta to discuss the future course of the campaign. Sigal agreed. At 0430 on the 4th, Sigal, all of five feet and six inches, and the six-foot, four-inch tall Wunderlin, who during the Atlantic crossing had become known as "Mutt and Jeff" to the crew of the *Mount Whitney*, met at II MEF forward headquarters at the Altafjord Vertshus.

At the meeting, Wunderlin expressed two major concerns. First, two regiments of the Soviet 111th

MRD were preparing to attack down the E-6 and along the Karasjok-Lakselv road. The best course of action, thought Wunderlin, would be for Sigal to step up the tempo of air strikes against the Soviet troop concentrations to delay the 111th MRD's attack until the MEF was concentrated.

Sigal, who agreed to the request, later wrote: "Hank wanted not just to beat off the Russians, but to destroy them."

Wunderlin's second concern was political:

I wanted to know what was expected of me when I reached the Russian border, and I assured Marc that I would do just that in a matter of days. Could I cross, or would I have to stop? He told me that while no final decision had yet been made, it appeared that the Norwegians would not support any advance into the Soviet Union and that in all probability I would have to halt. Marc also had heard rumors that Soviet diplomats in Sweden had contacted the Norwegian and Finnish ambassadors and had suggested a ceasefire in Norway and the withdrawal of all foreign troops from Finland. He said to me, "Hank, whatever you plan to do, do it in the next couple days."

The meeting with Sigal convinced Wunderlin that if he was to run the Russians out of northern Norway, he had to do it quickly. He set his staff to work drawing up plans for the rapid pursuit and destruction of the 111th MRD before it could retreat into the Kola, and the "liberation" of northern Norway as far as Kirkenes. He also issued an "Order of the Day" to his men.

To the Marines of II MEF:

We are here in northern Norway, British, Dutch, and American Marines, "soldiers of the sea" all, as representatives of an alliance of free peoples. Our mission is to drive the invader from the territory of our ally—Norway. Over the next few days I will call on you to push yourselves and your equipment to the limits of endurance, perhaps beyond the limits of endurance. But you must believe that I do so only with your interest in mind. We must keep the enemy on the run and allow him no chance to halt and prepare a defense that would be costly to storm. We must not just push him back, leaving destruction in his wake, we must insure that he will not repeat this aggression. We must run him out of Norway, destroy him before he retreats. We must finish him, here, in Finnmark.

At noon on the 4th, the 111th MRD's 339 Regiment attacked the 2nd battalion, 4th Marines, along the E-6 south of Borselv in an attempt to drive south to relieve the 45th Corps. Brigadier General Robert McMonagle, 4 MEB commander, recalled:

I watched the attack develop and thought to myself how clumsy the Russians seemed. Then I realized that these were the same tactics I had seen them employ against us when we first engaged them south of Bodo. During the intervening seven or eight days, I had watched our own tactics evolve as we learned a variety of lessons the hard way. Our prewar doctrine had been far from perfect.

Let's be honest, nobody had the picture of the next war right. But we were flexible enough to learn from our mistakes. In a week we had gotten damned good. But the Russians, they never seemed to learn anything. They just ran their drills over and over again. They hadn't worked the first time, and against my men, who were now veterans, they sure as hell were not going to work any better. We shot the hell out of them and then called in air.

On the morning of 5 August the other two battalions of 4 MEB landed near Borselv and blocked the retreat of the 339th Regiment. Caught between the two MEBs, by day's end the Soviet formation no longer existed as a fighting force.

USMC AH-1 Cobra gunship maneuvers into firing position. AH-1T carries a 20 mm gun, rockets, sidewinder, TOW, and Hellfire missiles.

The remnants of the 111th MRD then began to withdraw, the right wing to Kirkenes, the left to Karasjok. Since Sixth Army headquarters had joined the retreat of the 54th Corps through Finland, the LMD airmobile brigade moved back to Kaamenen, along the Karasjok-Ivalo road.

Determined as ever, Wunderlin drove his Marines hard to keep the Soviets off balance. 4 MEB drove north along E-6. By the evening of 7 August it had taken Tana, Nyborg, and Vadso and had reached Neiden, fifteen miles from Kirkenes.

Earlier that day, Fitzgerald's UK-NL Amphibious Force, at last operating together, moved by road and helicopter toward Karasjok, held by a battalion of the 111th MRD. With the support of an "airmobilized" Norwegian battalion from the 15th Brigade, 42 and 45 Commando and the Dutch Marine battalion drove the Soviets from the town and captured the Tana River bridge before Russian engineers were able to blow it.

Airmobile elements of 6 MEB then struck deep into Finnish Lapland, surprising the LMD airmobile brigade in what proved to be the final battle of the campaign in Norway. The remnants of two Soviet battalions were destroyed, their helicopters caught on the ground by Marine A-6s and F/A-18s. By the morning of 8 August, the 6th Marines were on the outskirts of Ivalo.

But here the Allied advance halted. As Vice Admiral Sigal had foreseen, the Norwegians were unwilling to carry the offensive across the Soviet border. Moreover, the Finns had no desire to see their country turned into a big-power battleground. Both Helsinki and Oslo accepted a Soviet proposal that called for:

1) Soviet withdrawal from Finland and Norway;
2) evacuation of all NATO forces from Finland;
3) and withdrawal of all non-Norwegian forces from Finnmark.

NATO military commanders on the Northern Flank, especially Hank Wunderlin, who had pushed to within a few hours of Kirkenes, were initially less than enthusiastic about the diplomatic accord. The momentum of the offensive seemed unstoppable, and the prospects of "rolling into the Kola" looked bright. But, as General Sir Ian Moore commented, "to what end?"

We were fighting a conventional war. We had already destroyed Soviet sea, air, and land forces. The Russians no longer posed a significant conventional threat to the North Atlantic SLOCs, nor to northern Norway. To push into the Kola would have to be seen as a move against their strategic assets. We had clear signals from Stockholm that it would be seen as such. And we had already decided not to seek out and destroy the Russian Boomers that had fled under the ice when we started operating our air over the Barents.

Of course, an end of the campaign on the Northern Flank freed up significant NATO forces for employment elsewhere. For example, I was particularly happy to be able to concentrate

AFNORTH air assets over the Baltic, given the desperate situation in BALTAP. This wasn't true for the Russians since their forces in Northwest TSMA, for the most part, had been destroyed.

Although it might be technically possible for the Soviets to move additional air and land forces to the Kola and renew their attacks, it seemed unlikely that they would do so given their recent experiences and the situation on the other fronts.

For their part, the Norwegians had good reason to accept a proposal to end the war on the Northern Flank. Their army in the north was exhausted and had suffered about half of the 13,000 NATO ground casualties incurred during the twenty days of fighting. Fewer than half of COMNON's Norwegian units were considered capable of sustained offensive action, and few of the reservists, who had been steadfast in the defense of their homeland, were anxious to invade the Soviet Union. Half the Norwegian Air Force was out of action. And the bulk of the Norwegian Navy lay on the bottom of the Norwegian Sea.

Nevertheless, NATO had won a tremendous victory in the twenty-day campaign on the Northern Flank. The Soviet Army had been driven out of Norway and Finland. The 45th Corps and 76th Guards Airborne Division had been destroyed. And three of the 54th Corps' brigades had been decimated. In all, the Sixth Army suffered approximately 34,000 casualties during the course of the campaign.

At sea, the critical North Atlantic SLOCs had been secured. Only a few damaged cruisers and destroyers, and some frigates and corvettes, remained of the once powerful Soviet Northern Fleet. The *Tblisi*, *Frunze* and over thirty submarines had been sunk.

Well over half of the SNA's aircraft had been

destroyed, including two-thirds of the Badgers and Backfires capable of attacking the North Atlantic SLOCs. And, except for some old MiG-21s flown in from the south, Soviet air power in the Kola had been smashed.

For the Soviet Union, the campaign in the north had ended in unmitigated disaster symbolized, perhaps, by the death of Marshal Vladimirov on 2 August.

Epilogue

A Triphibious Masterpiece

Fortunately for the United States, the Third World War in the early 1990s proved neither apocalyptic nor protracted. Nevertheless, the war was characterized by a series of bitter struggles waged in space, in the air, on land, under the world's seas and on their surface. The three-dimensional campaign on NATO's northern flank was crucial to victory by the allies.

In the end, the maritime powers, the United States and its allies, persevered and triumphed. The Soviet bid for Eurasian hegemony failed.

That the new Tsars still rule in the Kremlin is testimony not to their military prowess, but simply to their possession of nuclear weapons, instruments of destruction so horrific that no military campaign to destroy the Soviet regime could have been risked.

If anything, allied victory in the Third World War was a triumph of sea power, particularly American sea power. This was especially true on the European flanks. Allied naval successes in the Atlantic and the Norwegian Sea, the Mediterranean and the Aegean, and the Indian

Ocean achieved results beyond their immediate scope. They secured victories in Norway, North Africa, the Levant, the Balkans, Anatolia, Mesopotamia, and the northern shores of the Gulf.

The Pacific war, too, was won on the high seas. Even in the ground war fought on the Korean peninsula the Allies owed their victory to their command of the sea lines of communication.

On the Central Front, NATO ground and air forces did defeat the main Warsaw Pact forces driving for the Rhine. But the American supplies and reinforcements to sustain the successful Allied counterattack that eventually crushed the Pact's offensive were carried across an ocean secured by Allied naval forces. Without victory in the battle of the Atlantic, the late summer triumphs in Germany and the Balkans would have never come about.

The campaign on the northern flank might have been the most impressive of all. In the words of Chief of Naval Operations Admiral Frank G. Dunn, conveyed in his official report to the President, it was "a triphibious masterpiece."

No doubt, the war in the northeastern Atlantic and northern Norway will long remain a classic example of strategic planning, logistic preparation, and joint and combined operational execution. The Allied victory capped over four decades of NATO planning.

The northern victory also vindicated the concepts of American naval strategists. Those who, in the decade before the war, had criticized the U.S. Navy's Maritime Strategy for advocating offensive operations north of the G-I-UK Gap were proven wrong. While few critics ever questioned the existence of a Soviet threat to American ships in the northeastern Atlantic, many argued before the war that carrier battle groups could not survive north of the Gap.

One thing did, however, become crystal clear during the course of the campaign; the United States Navy had little choice but to challenge the Soviets in the far north. The dangers NATO's navies faced in the Norwegian and Barents Seas could not be ignored, nor could the threats faced by Allied air and ground forces operating against the Soviets in northern Norway.

As Admiral Dunn remarked at the news conference following the release of the unclassified summary of his findings:

There was one critic who always argued that sending the Navy into the Norwegian Sea was akin to pitting "strength against strength," and that was bad strategy. His idea of good strategy involved sending our tanks up against the Red Army in Germany. Now, to my mind, if that's not "pitting strength against strength," I don't know what it is.

People just have this thing about ships getting sunk. I think it was Churchill who wrote about the initial attack on the Turks at the Dardanelles in 1915 and asked why it was acceptable for the generals to throw away the lives of a quarter of a million infantrymen in fruitless assaults on entrenched Germans, but it was considered reckless to risk a few ships in an effort to force the Straits.

Strategy involves risk. In war men get killed, planes get shot down, tanks get knocked out, and ships get sunk. At the professional level, I felt comfortable taking those risks. Even at the personal level, I'll tell you this; I was much less concerned knowing my son was on a carrier in the Norwegian Sea than I would have been had he been in a tank in the Fulda Gap.

Appendix

Politics, Strategy and Forces

The Northern Flank played a critical role in Soviet grand strategy. A successful Arctic offensive, combined with victory in Germany, would make a protracted conflict unlikely, for the Soviets would be well positioned to conduct a war of attrition should the Americans and any contingent of NATO allies wish to continue the struggle.

Even if the initial operational thrust across the Inter-German Border (IGB) failed, a victorious campaign in the north might provide the Soviets with a second chance to triumph on the Central Front since they would then be in position to disrupt Allied use of the North Atlantic Sea Lines of Communications (SLOCs).

Defensive considerations also shaped Soviet plans for the Northern Flank. The northern approaches to the USSR had to be secured against NATO bombing and cruise missile attacks. The Kola bases of Soviet ballistic missile submarines and their Arctic bastion also had to be protected. The only sea route not easily severed by the U.S. Navy—the Arctic passage tying the Soviet Far East to European Russia—had to be safeguarded.

To achieve their goals on the Northern Flank, the Soviets had to overcome three major disadvantages: first, the geography of the region favored the defender; second, the Soviets could not be certain that they would be able to maintain throughout the campaign the quantitative superiority they would hold at the outset; and third, their command structure all but ensured poor coordination of forces.

Geography provided the Norwegians with the strategic depth that NATO lacked on the Central Front. The northern area of Norway, which had literally been leveled by the Germans during their retreat from Finland in 1944, was underpopulated and contained little of strategic value. Finnmark, a high glacier-scarred plateau, presented the Soviets with few defenders. Only a weak Norwegian formation, the South Varanger Garrison, a battalion-sized defense force, covered the frontier near Kirkenes.

For the Soviets to reach their geographic objectives in the north, they had to advance as far as Narvik, preferably to Bodo, and occupy most of the Fydde, the three northern counties of Norway: Finnmark, Troms, and Nordland.

Troops of the 45th Corps, concentrated in the Pechenga-Murmansk area, began the war over 250 miles from the main NATO defensive lines in Troms. But these direct distances are deceptive, for the E-6, the only major road in northern Norway, winds its way along a coast indented by numerous fiords. The road distance from the Soviet border to Tromso is about 550 miles, to Narvik 700, and to Bodo well over 800.

The 54th Corps, concentrated around Kandalaska, was positioned to drive across Finnish Lapland, but faced somewhat more difficult terrain, in spite of the shorter road distances. In comparison, the Soviet drive across West Germany traversed on

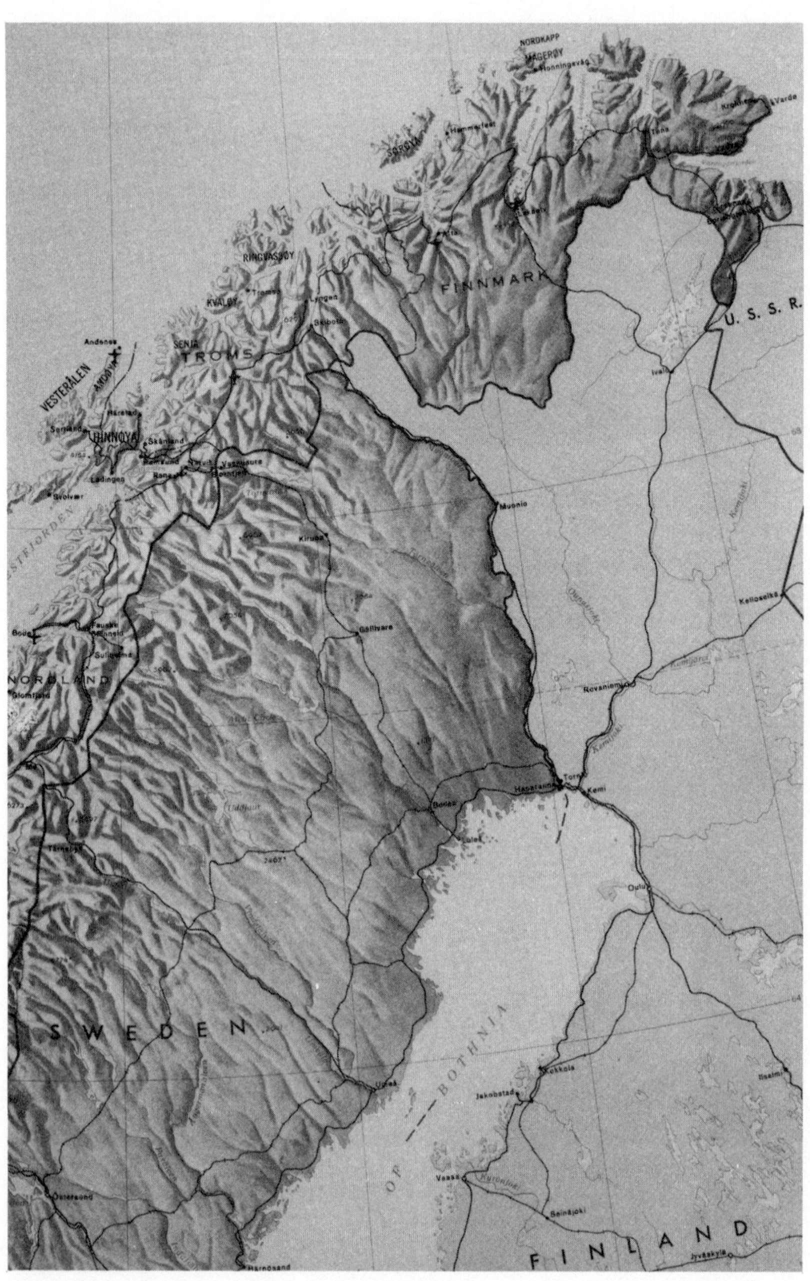
NORDKAPP
MAGERØY
Honningsvåg
Vardø
Hammerfest
SØRØYA
RINGVASSØY
FINNMARK
U. S. S. R.
KVALØY
Tromsø
Lyngen
Skibotn
Andenes
SENJA
TROMS
VESTERÅLEN
ANDØYA
Harstad
Sortland
HINNØYA
Skånland
Lødingen
Svolvær
Ivalo
Muonio
Kiruna
Gällivare
Bodø
Fauske
Sulitjelma
NORDLAND
Glomfjord
Rovaniemi
Haparanda
Tornio
Kemi
Boden
Luleå
Oulu
SWEDEN
OF BOTHNIA
Umeå
Kokkola
Jakobstad
Vaasa
Seinäjoki
FINLAND
Jyväskylä
Östersund
Härnösand

average about 170 miles, only 140 at the narrowest point in the south.

Any ground war on the Northern Flank would have to be fought entirely north of the Arctic Circle where military operations are particularly treacherous. Survivors of the only major Arctic campaigns during the Second World War bore testimony to the harsh conditions they confronted in the forbidding Arctic climate.

A 1959 U.S. Army pamphlet on German operations in the northern theater from 1940-1945 succinctly described the peculiar difficulties any military would have to overcome to successfully conduct operations in this intemperate region:

1. In the Arctic the human element is all-important. The effectiveness of motorized and mechanized equipment is greatly reduced; the chief reliance must always be on men, not machines. Specialized training and experience are essential. The climate allows no margin of error either for the individual or for the organization as a whole.

Movement in Northern Norway is restricted to a sparse network of all-weather roads.

2. The mobility of units, large or small, is low. Maneuvers must be precisely planned and executed with the knowledge that distance can be as difficult to overcome as the enemy. Momentum is difficult to achieve and quickly lost.

3. Control of space is unimportant. Roads are difficult to build, and operations inevitably center around those few which already exist or can be constructed. One good line of communications can be decisive.

4. There is no favorable season for operations. Climate and terrain are always enemies, particularly to offensive operations. The winter is relatively favorable in one respect, namely that the snow and ice make rapid movement by specially trained and equipped troops possible. Throughout much of the winter, however, operations must be conducted in near-total darkness. The most satisfactory period is in the late winter when the days are lengthening; but then time is limited, and operations must be completed or abandoned at the onset of the spring thaw.

Earl F. Ziemke, The German Northern Theater of Operations, 1940-1945 (Washington, Department of the Army Pamphlet No. 20-271, 1959), p. 317.

The Soviets planned to launch their campaign in midsummer. July and August are the two warmest months of the year, with temperatures averaging about 54° F. The absence of life-threatening cold certainly made many aspects of operational movement much easier. But the summer was also the rainy season, the average annual rainfall for July and August being about 5 inches. Cloud cover was the norm. The combination of thaw and rain made off-road movement difficult, and in some areas impossible. A further complication were the frequent heavy fogs that moved into the coastal areas, and over the coastal roads, during the summer months.

Thus the Soviets had to conquer the Arctic before they even reached the main line of Norwegian resistance. It lay north of Narvik, in mountainous Troms, where less than 20 miles separated the Lyngen Fiord from the Finnish border. In 1944 the Germans had taken their stand here following their retreat from Finland. Often dubbed Fortress Norway, the area included the Norwegians' main northern naval base, Olavsvern (Tromso), the ports of Narvik and Harstad, and the important air bases at Bardufoss, Andoya, and Evenes.

It was in Fortress Norway that the Norwegian Army would concentrate to defend the country in the event of a Soviet invasion. Many Home Guard units, which made up the bulk of the Norwegian Army, had their equipment stored within, and would fly, motor, or walk, to their

Norwegian regular and reserve forces, like this antitank crew, delayed the Soviet advance by their valiant fight.

mobilization sites. NATO reinforcements also would arrive by land, air, and sea.

After traversing Finnmark, the Soviet Army would confront this strong NATO position. Mountains, some as high as 5,000 feet, were cut by a single road, the E-6 extension north of Narvik constructed by the Germans during the Second World War--the Reichstrasse 50. The Soviets, if they wished to maintain any significant rate of advance with their nearly entirely mechanized forces, would see their drive channeled as they approached Fortress Norway.

Norwegian geography not only limited movement, but also posed restrictions on the commitment and use of Soviet ground forces in the theater.

Soviet T-80 tank, with reactive armor, was limited to road movement in the far north, negating its mobility and shock effects.

Soviet conventional strength rested primarily in their Army, a well equipped, well indoctrinated force prepared to fight its way west across the European plain, much as it had during the Second World War. Given the distances and the nature of the terrain to be crossed, it was simply impossible to deploy a ground force on the Northern Flank

of sufficient size to achieve the favorable ratio of forces that were common along the IGB.

Moreover, the equipment and doctrine adopted for the war on the Central Front were not particularly suited to conflict in the Arctic. In the late 1980s the Soviets had come to the conclusion that their ground forces needed to be reorganized

The MI-28 Havoc attack helicopter proved useful in surmounting terrain obstacles, but was hampered by fog and low ceilings.

and restructured to insure effective combined-arms operations on the Central Front. In first echelon formations, standard division and regimental organization had given way to flexible corps and brigade structures that permitted battalions and even companies of different arms to be brought together under a brigade headquarters. A com-

mander was able to tailor a force to the task at hand, taking into account distances, terrain, and the strength of the defense. But while this more flexible organization was well suited to northern operations and was welcomed by Soviet commanders in the Kola, the doctrine that went with it—Operational Maneuver Groups (OMGs) and

Echeloned Assault—was of little use in Norway. The distances to be covered and the inability to move cross country were major operational problems peculiar to the region. Moreover, moving and maintaining a mechanized corps along a single road, hundreds of miles from its depots, posed major logistical problems unseen in Germany that made alternative means of movement and resupply—air and sea—critically important.

The Soviets planned to commit forty-two maneuver battalions—twenty-four of the 45th and 54th Corps, nine of the 76th Guard Airborne Division, four of the Leningrad Military District's (LMD) Airmobile Brigade, and five of Naval Infantry—to operations in north Norway.

But Stavka planners recognized that their northern assault could face as many as forty NATO battalions in north Norway. The Norwegian Army alone, if allowed to mobilize fully, would field twenty-seven battalions in the north. NATO reinforcements raised the total. Battalions from the NATO reserve mobile forces and US Marine Expeditionary Brigades would bring NATO forces to a strength of forty battalions. Additional United States Marine and Army light infantry battalions, or elements of the UK Mobile Force could also be deployed to Norway.

The NATO troops were as well equipped and better trained than their Soviet counterparts. The Norwegians knew the terrain and were prepared to fight in the mountains. Reinforcing NATO units were mostly elite commandos, marines, and paratroopers, long-service regulars, many of whom took part in maneuvers in the region on a yearly basis. The Soviets would be hard put to bludgeon these units out of strong mountain positions.

To break through and push on toward Narvik and Bodo, Stavka planned to circumvent the

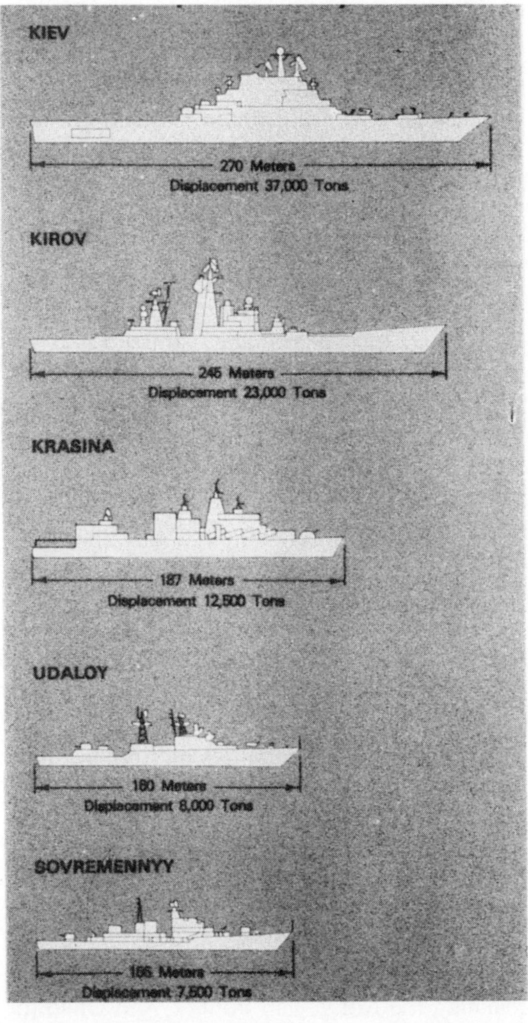

Comparison of major Soviet surface ship classes.

Norwegian fortress region and prevent NATO and Norwegian reinforcements from reaching the area. The Soviets had a variety of options. They could violate Finnish or Swedish neutrality, move naval infantry by sea, or paratroopers by air to positions in the Norwegian rear.

Violating Finnish neutrality involved only

moderate risk. Finland was not a particularly strong country and its forces in the north were weak, essentially a single battalion. Only a violation of the relatively uninhabited extreme northern part of Finland was necessary. Even if the Finns failed to acquiesce to a Soviet demand for free passage, they were unlikely to do much about it. Soviet forces in the LMD were more than adequate to prevent Finnish interference in the movement into Norway. And the Finns were unlikely to launch hostilities farther south and expand the war into the heart of their country.

But crossing Finland was of marginal help to Soviet planners. The small "Finnish Wedge," traversed by a single road, the E-78, led to Skibotn where it connected with the E-6 near the head of the Lyngen Fiord. From there the Soviets still had to drive another 60 road miles southward to Bardufoss and 110 to Narvik. The threat of such an enfilading movement, while it increased the length of the NATO line to about 25 miles of still defensible mountainous terrain, was unlikely to prove decisive.

An invasion of neutral Sweden would have allowed the Soviets to bypass the Lyngen position entirely and thrust to the coast south of Narvik. But a Swedish armed response would have caused the Soviets trouble, and not only in the far north. They would have had to cut through several hundred miles of swamp, woods, and mountains defended by the Swedish Army before even reaching the Norwegian frontier. And while the Soviet Army could easily threaten the populated regions of Finland, the same was not true of Sweden. Most importantly, Sweden's entry into the war as an active participant would have had a direct impact on the battle to the south. The Leningrad Front would have to have been committed through Finland and into Sweden, thus taking reserve forces from the campaign in Germany. An active Swedish Air Force and Navy would have made Warsaw Pact operations in the Baltic more difficult, especially those aimed at Denmark. For these reasons, Soviet planners ruled out the Swedish option for a general war.

Denied an overland solution to this strategic dilemma, the Soviets looked to the mobility of their naval and air forces. The main attack would follow the direct routes through Finnmark (the 45th Corps) and Finnish Lapland (the 54th Corps). On D-Day elements of the 76th Guards Airborne Division would land at Bodo, Narvik, and Tromso. Lead elements of the Northern Fleet's naval infantry brigade would embark at Kola ports, round the North Cape, and land on Andoy in the Vesteralen (Western Islands) and seize the NATO airfield at Andoya, and elsewhere in the Lofotens, closing the Ofot Fiord approaches to Narvik. Follow-up units would reinforce the air and sea bridgeheads. Not only would the main Norwegian position be bypassed, but NATO reinforcements would be prevented from reaching the Fortress Norway area. The United States' 4th MEB, which was supposed to fly into Vaernes airfield near Trondheim to marry up with its equipment, was expected to reach the area near Bodo in about four to six days. However, it would find its way blocked by the 76th Guards at Bodo. The Soviet Navy would contest control of the Norwegian Sea and in combination with the Naval Infantry Brigade would prevent NATO reinforcement through Narvik. Soviet air units would gain local air superiority, neutralize Norwegian airfields in north Norway, and prevent NATO reinforcement by air. The resistance of the isolated Norwegian forces would crumble. North Norway would be securely in Soviet hands.

But in the air and on the sea the Soviets were

Tu-95 Bear H bomber, in addition to its long range reconnaissance capabilities, carries cruise missiles.

little better off than they were on the ground. The number of Soviet aircraft deployed in the far north, about 1,000, was impressive, but less than fully indicative of fighting power. Many Soviet planes were pure fighters or bombers, while most NATO aircraft were multi-functional. The Soviets deployed about 700 aircraft in the

far north.

Not all of these aircraft were actually available to support operations in Norway or in the Atlantic. Of the 150 aircraft of the Leningrad Military District, about a third were obsolete MiG-21 Fishbeds, another third Su-17 Fitter ground attack aircraft,and only 50 modern fighters. Moreover,

Yak-38 Forger on rainswept flight deck. Yak-38 was no match for the British and U.S. Harrier V/STOL

few of the aircraft of the LMD were deployed to the Kola in peacetime, when the squadrons rotated to northern airfields for training and exercise. During the war, only about a third of the LMD's planes were moved north, the rest remained in Front reserve, in support of the 30th Army Corps deployed opposite southern Finland to keep the Finns from moving forces to the north, while others were drawn into the struggle in the Baltic. About sixty air defense fighters were deployed in the Archangelsk area, too far from north Norway to be used effectively. Of the 140 aircraft actually deployed in the Kola, about seventy-five were Fitters, although many of the remainder were the most modern types

in the Soviet arsenal, MiG-29 Fulcrums and MiG-31 Foxhounds. But those planes bore primary responsibility for the air defense of the Kola and the Soviet homeland. They were never all free to support operations in north Norway or the Atlantic.

American Department of Defense (DoD) publications generally assigned about 450 aircraft to the Soviet Northern Fleet. But minus types such as helicopters, transports, ASW aircraft, reconnaissance planes, and mine laying aircraft, the Northern Fleet deployed only fifty obsolescent Tu-16 Badgers, thirty mediocre Yak-38 Forgers, and 15 Su-27 Flankers from its bases in the Kola and from its carrier. The Forgers, carrier VTOL

Backfire strategic bomber was a formidable threat to the allied surface fleets, with its AS-4 air-to-surface missiles.

aircraft with miserable endurance and poor maneuverability, were hardly worth counting. In addition, about 100 Badger, Backfire, and Blackjack bombers from the Soviet strategic reserve were committed to the Kola in a naval strike role during the campaign.

Thus, of the 700 Soviet aircraft in the far north, only about 540 were actually available to support operations on the Northern Flank, and of these, only about 200, including thirty Forgers, were fighters.

The failure of the Northern Fleet to control its own modern fighters, other than the mediocre Yak-38s and the handful of Flankers deployed on the nuclear carrier *Tblisi*, proved to be a major

handicap during the campaign. A great deal of the striking power of the Soviet Navy lay in its aviation assets. As naval strike bombers, Badgers and Backfires were originally designed to conduct stand-off attacks with nuclear air-to-surface missiles as part of a coordinated air, surface, and subsurface strike against American carriers. The bombers were not truly strike planes as much as they were platforms for missiles that could be launched well beyond the range of American defensive systems. As an example, the vaunted Backfires and the older Badgers carried air-to-surface missiles (ASM) such as the AS-4 Kitchen and AS-6 Kingfish which had ranges of 250 nautical miles (nm). But the Downbeat radar of the Backfire

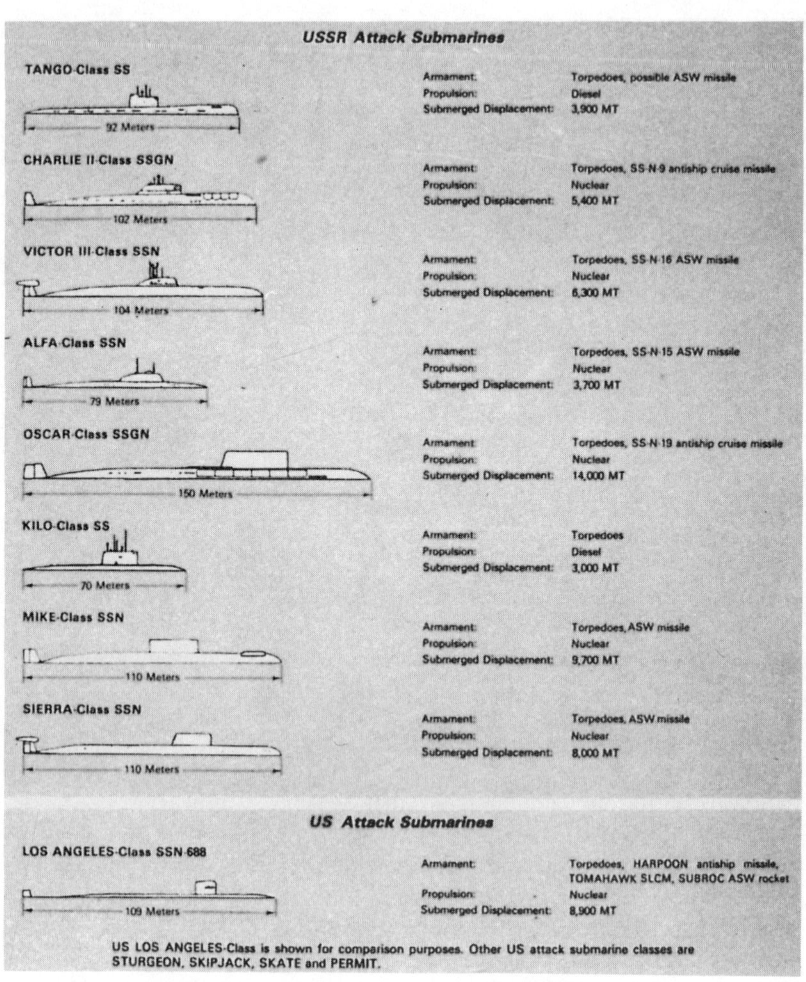

Soviet attack submarines compared with U.S. Los Angeles class SSN.

had an effective range of less than 175 nm, and the Badgers were equipped with radars that had 100nm maximum ranges.

Under the Soviet command system, a shore-based Fleet Command Post (KPF) coordinated the movements of Soviet air, surface, and subsurface forces. The movements of detected enemy forces were monitored, tracked in Soviet parlance, while strike platforms were guided into attack positions. Surface units in the vicinity, or air reconnaissance platforms, such as the Tu-95D Bear, were intended to provide the terminal guidance for the air-launched AS-4s and AS-6s to bring them to their targets.

The Soviet doctrine of combined attack suffered from several weaknesses. First, the belief that complicated multi-platform strikes could be centrally directed from a shore-based command post proved unfounded. Second, in a one-shot atomic struggle, precision and bomber survivability mattered little, but in a conventional conflict, strikes against naval forces operating with air cover were likely to be less decisive and placed a greater premium on bomber survival. Soviet Badgers, which were no longer in production, and Backfires, of which only thirty-six new planes were produced each year, were irreplaceable in a short war.

The Soviet penchant for trailing major NATO surface forces with expendable ships capable of providing the terminal guidance needed was also a tactic best suited to an atomic war at sea where the initial salvo was expected to prove decisive. In a conventional war, such shadowing vessels were destroyed in short order. Maintaining surface units for an extended period in active detection range of NATO task forces proved beyond Soviet capability. Nor were the fifty Bears based in the Kola adequate to the task, nor considered expendable.

The Northeastern Atlantic proved to be a graveyard for Soviet Tu-95s. Minus their surface or airborne "eyes," attacks by Soviet strike bombers against NATO task forces had to penetrate to within at least 175nm. Against surface forces operating beyond the range of land-based fighters,

Norwegian F-16 Falcons of the Royal Norwegian Air Force (KNL) struck the first air-to-air blows against the initial Soviet air attacks.

the Badgers and Backfires were still able to launch their missiles well beyond SAM range. But Soviet strikes against NATO surface forces operating within range of fighters based in Iceland, the United Kingdom, or Norway, or against American carrier battle groups (CVBGs), ran the risk of interception and destruction.

As Captain Second Class Anatoly Pushkin wrote:
If there were any SNA pilots who were anxious to fly their (Backfires) to within 175 miles of an American carrier with its F-14s on patrol, I failed to make their acquaintance. That was considered suicide.

Not long into the campaigns in the Northeastern

The Harrier V/STOL aircraft proved itself in the Faulklands War of 1982, and again in the campaign in north Norway.

Atlantic, the Mediterranean, the Indian Ocean, and the Pacific, the Soviets learned, frequently the hard way, that their bombers needed fighter escort even to force penetrations of what were frequently overstretched Allied CAPs. Unfortunately, such air support depended on the cooperation of Soviet Frontal Aviation or Air Defense Force

units. On the Northern Flank, support for SNA strikes proved to be a tertiary mission.

To face the Soviet's 700 aircraft in the air over Norway, NATO had earmarked about 400 fighter bombers and 100 other types for possible deployment on the Northern Flank. The Norwegian Air Force deployed about 100 modern fighters,

Total number of Soviet ships assigned to the Northern Fleet and NATO ships deployed into the theatre during the course of operations

Type	Soviet	Nato
Aircraft carrier	2	6
Battle ship/ cruiser	1	1
Cruisers	12	8
Destroyers	18	22
Frigates	17	42
Patrol combatant	25	12
Attack submarines	126	27

F-16s and F-5s, although not all of these were available for operations in the north. Potential NATO reinforcements included the supporting air element of II Marine Expeditionary Force (MEF) (as many as 13 USMC squadrons), 8 USAF squadrons, 8 British squadrons, and a Dutch squadron, that totalled more than 500 planes, almost all fighter-bombers. Thus, while the Soviets held an advantage in the overall number of land-based aircraft, in fighters and fighter-bombers NATO could hold a slight edge in overall quality and quantity.

The balance of forces in the air war in the far north would depend on two factors: the degree of Soviet success in early operations designed to knock out or capture NATO airfields, especially the USAF's designated Collocated Operating Bases (COB) at Bodo, Andoya, Evenes, and Bardufoss; and the extent of Soviet success on other fronts that might force SACEUR to commit reinforcing squadrons elsewhere.

The deployment of U.S. Navy carrier battle groups to the Norwegian Sea could, on the other

German	Neth.	Norway	Canada	U.K.	U.S.A.
—	—	—	—	2	4
—	—	—	—	—	1
—	—	—	—	—	8
1	1	—	2	6	12
—	7	4	3	13	15
—	—	12	—	—	—
—	—	7	—	8	12

hand, give NATO the clear upper hand in the air. An American carrier's complement of aircraft totals about eighty-five, including all types. About half of the aircraft are modern fighters, F-14s and F/A-18s. The four carriers ultimately deployed to the Norwegian Sea, with their 300+ fixed-wing aircraft, including 170 fighters, gave NATO a significant edge over the Soviets.

Whether or not the American aircraft carriers reached the Norwegian Sea depended on the course of the naval war in the North Atlantic. But here, too, the Soviets found themselves facing at least a marginal numerical disadvantage.

During the course of the campaign on the Northern Flank, the Soviets deployed most of the ships of their Northern Fleet, except for a few in the shipyards when the conflict began. NATO, not surprisingly, mustered superior carrier and surface forces in the Northeastern Atlantic. But even in the area of submarines, NATO achieved parity.

Of the Soviet Northern Fleet's 126 nuclear and diesel-powered attack and cruise missile-armed

Variety of helicopters on the flight deck of USS Saipan. Boat deck, capable of carrying several landing craft, is visible.

submarines, nineteen were being repaired, overhauled, or modernized in various yards. Twenty-five were detached to Arctic patrols escorting Soviet SSBNs in the northern bastion. While this number appears excessive, the Soviet practice had long been to escort each SSBN with a SSN. Another twenty-three submarines were assigned to the Mediterranean, where the crisis had originated, and were in or on their way to the Middle Sea when the war began. Eleven submarines were deployed astride the North Atlantic routes leading to the Bay of Biscay and the English Channel. Seven patrolled off the American east coast, five in the Caribbean, and four in the South Atlantic. Thus, of the 126 submarines of the Northern Fleet, only thirty-two were available for operations between the Greenland-Iceland-UK Gap and the Arctic during the campaign.